... YOUR MODEL PONIES ALL HAVE THEIR HISTORIES ON A SPREADSHEET

... YOU REFUSE TO GO ON HOLIDAY WITH YOUR FAMILY UNTIL YOU'VE BOOKED A RIDE ON THE BEACH

... YOU CAN DRAW BRILLIANT HORSES (BUT NOTHING ELSE)

...YOUR PHONE'S RINGTONE IS THE THEME TO BLACK BEAUTY

... ALL YOUR CHRISTMAS AND BIRTHDAY PRESENTS COME FROM A TACK SHOP

... YOU SPEND THE LAST OF YOUR POCKET MONEY ON APPLES AND CARROTS FOR YOU-KNOW-WHO

... YOU TELL YOUR FAVE PONY SECRETS YOU WOULD NEVER EVEN TRUST YOUR BFF WITH

... YOU HAVE THE RIDING SCHOOL ON SPEED

... YOUR S   ECTS ARE ALL ABOUT HORSES

... YOUR RIDING BOOTS ARE SPOTLESS AND GLEAMING – BUT YOUR REGULAR SHOES ARE SCUFFED AND DIRTY

... YOU ONLY EVER WEAR JODPHUR BOOTS WITH YOUR JEANS

... YOU EAT MUSELI BECAUSE IT LOOKS LIKE YOUR PONY'S COARSE MIX

... YOU'D RATHER SNOG A PONY THAN A BOY (IT'S A NO BRAINER!!!)

HELP!

... YOU KNOW, WITH ABSOLUTE CERTAINTY, THAT IF THERE WERE NO HORSES, YOU WOULD SIMPLY CEASE TO EXIST ...

3

PONY: The Annual

First published in Great Britain in 2015
DJ Murphy (Publishers) Ltd

ISBN-978-0-9928279-2-2

Who did what in **PONY: The Annual!**

Editorial: **Janet Rising, Laura Hodgson**
Design: **Paul Smail, Callum Cussen**
Published by: **DJ Murphy (Publishers) Ltd**, Marlborough House,
Headley Road, Grayshott, Surrey GU26 6LG

Printed by: **Graphicom via dell'Industria – 36100 Vicenza, Italy**

Photography: **DJ Murphy, Bob Atkins, Trevor Meeks, Shutterstock.com**
Front cover image by **Bob Atkins**
Illustrators: **Helena Öhmark and Rebecca Enström** (26, 52, 74, 92)

PONY Magazine is published every four weeks.
To find out more about **PONY Magazine**, visit **www.ponymag.com**

PONY

2016
The Annual

PONY ANNUAL 2016

WHAT'S IN YOUR PONY ANNUAL?

Start small

Top eventers didn't begin at Badminton – they worked their way up through small competitions, practising on tiny jumps and perfecting their technique. You can't skip the basics, so begin now – how about that pile of twigs over there?

Join a club

The Pony Club is brilliant for both instruction and competitions – and you'll be in an environment that fosters good competitive spirit, too. But there are riding clubs, and riding school clubs which can help you. So get out there and join!

Wear the right kit

Never compromise your own safety, or that of your pony. Make sure his tack fits him well, and is in good repair. Ensure the farrier visits regularly, and fit studs if you need to – and don't forget to get him fit and feed him according to his workload so he can carry you around a course. You need to wear the right kit, too. A crash hat, gloves and a body protector or, if you can run to it, an inflatable air jacket. You want to be safe!

Be an ace cross country rider!

Fancy yourself as the next Zara or Mary? Here are some ways to get ahead of the game right now!

Be honest with yourself

Are you a brave rider? A rider who enjoys jumping and galloping and taking on a challenge? Practice will make you more familiar with riding across country but if you're really not the thrusting type, then maybe it's time to face reality and take up something a little less demanding. There are plenty of other disciplines in which you can excel!

Get fit

An unfit rider is heavier and more tiring for your pony to carry. Not only does your pony have to be fit, but you do, too. Eat well, keep your fitness up and your pony will find it easier to go faster and jump better for you.

Learn the techniques

Riding across country is very different to show jumping – so take some lessons. For a start, you will need to ride in a forward seat when you are cantering between fences. Shorten your stirrups and take the weight on your knees, through to your heels. It's a tiring position, so get used to it at home.

Learn how to jump different fences

There are always lots of different types of fences on a cross country course and each one needs to be tackled differently. Have some lessons (and watch other people) to learn the techniques. It will pay off in the end.

Walk the course

Even if you are not riding in an event, if you can trail other riders and listen to what they have to say, you will learn loads about how they intend to ride the course. You might also be able to join a coursewalk with a famous rider – and what they can tell you will be a real eye-opener!

Good luck – see you at Badminton one day!

Pony care basics

Mucking out

Come on now, get the worst chore done first! Even mucking out can be okay if you focus on the good bits – a nice bed at the end of it. Here are some top tips for professional mucking out.

● **Tie your pony up *outside* the stable.**

● Take the wheelbarrow into the empty stable so you don't spread dirty bedding everywhere.

● **Put as much manure and soiled bedding in the wheelbarrow and press it down so it doesn't blow about.**

● If you can leave the floor to dry – great!

● **Mixing clean bedding with the damp stuff will fluff it all up.**

● Put down a good, deep bed. This aids drainage, is better for your pony's legs and encourages him to lie down. Thin beds are rubbish and get dirty quicker.

● **Bank the sides to encourage your pony to lie in the centre and to discourage draughts.**

● Sweep up, empty your barrow, tidy the muck heap and the job's done!

● **Skipping out throughout the day helps your mucking out tomorrow!**

10

Feeding

Haynets
● Buy lots so you can fill them at the weekend, ready to hang in the week. BUT – if you soak your hay, only do it on the day you feed each net.
● **Weigh your haynet!**
● Check the drawstring regularly for wear.

Short feed
● Weigh your pony's feed.
● **Don't over-feed!**
● Feed your pony for the work he does.
● **Keep feed buckets clean.**

Grooming

If time is short, concentrate on the basics:
● Pick out hooves.
● **Brush his head and where the saddle goes.**
● Sponge the eyes, nose and dock.
● **Brush out the mane and tail.**
● Brush stable stains with a body brush – give it some welly and they'll come off!
● **Never brush wet mud! Wait for it to dry.**
● Give your pony a good groom every three days or so.

Yard duties

● **Always put your tools away for safety.**
● Sweep up and weed regularly, to keep everywhere ship-shape.
● **Tidy up headcollars – hang them up (not on the ground!).**
● Put things away. You shouldn't be falling over buckets, mangers, coats, bales of bedding or hay, tack or tools – and neither should your pony. Keep it tidy, keep it safe!
● **Ensure fire notices and equipment are visible and serviced.**

Field duties

● **How's your fencing? Check it daily!**
● Walk around the field at *least* once a week to check for poisonous plants, litter and anything unusual.
● **Check troughs every day, twice a day, especially if ponies live out 24/7.**
● Ensure gates are well cared for – and swing easily.
● **Keep fields clear of dung – poo-pick weekly – more often if you can!!**

Tack cleaning

No time to clean tack every day? Make sure your pony's bit is always rinsed under the tap after every ride, and change his numnah and girth for clean ones frequently to keep him comfortable. Give your tack a thorough clean at the weekend – take it apart and check all the stitching!

Remember!
Keeping on top of these chores every day takes only a few minutes, but keeps your pony safe and happy – and the yard tidy!

STAR STUDENT
School rules!

Whether you have your own pony, or ride at a riding school, you need to know the rules of the school!

What rules?

Riding in the school or manège would be very confusing if the riders didn't know the rules. Rules mean that everyone can ride in harmony and accidents and misunderstandings are kept to a minimum. Riding by the rules is essential!

Knock before you enter!

With some schools it's impossible to see what's going on as you and your pony join the party. So rule one is always to knock and ask whether it is safe to open the door and enter. Some doors are noisy, and ponies may spook.

Stand in the centre

Always take your pony to the middle of the school when you are preparing him to be ridden. That way, the riders working their ponies can use the outside track and no-one collides. It is safest to line up facing a long side, well away from any other ponies.

Plan your ride

Once you are settled in the saddle, ensure you know what you are going to do. That way you can set off purposefully, rather than dither about and get in someone's way.

Slow paces = inside track

If working at a slow pace or giving your pony a breather, use the inside track (about two metres from the outside). That way, faster ponies can use the outside track, which is easier for them.

Pass left-hand to left-hand

You're not expected to all ride around on the same rein. When passing another rider, always ensure you pass with your left hand closest to their left hand. This means that riders on the right rein need to move onto the inside track to pass riders on the left rein.

PERFECT!

No stopping!

Do not halt on the outside track. You could cause a pile-up if someone is working behind you. Ride to the centre and stop there.

Be considerate

All riders should be aware of other school users. Look about you! More experienced riders should always give way to less experienced riders and if you see another rider having problems with a lively pony, don't ride your pony fast, or too close.

Keep your distance

Always keep at least a pony's length between ponies.

GREAT JOB!

Ride with a friend

It is never a good idea to school alone. Always make sure someone else (not necessarily mounted) is with you when schooling, for safety.

Shut that door!

Always close the door or gate to the school when riding. Never leave a gate ajar as a pony could try to go through it, hurting himself and his rider.

Find your own space!

If the pony in front of you is going slower than you, turn across the school and find a space, rather than getting too close.

Keep out of the way!

Do not get in the way of riders working on circles or other school movements. They, in turn, should do the same for you!

You're 'avin' a giraffe!

Everyone knows that horses and ponies have a sense of humour. If you don't believe us, just look at this little lot!

I've got fringe benefits

Me and mini me!

Get ahead... get a hat!

I'd recommend that teeth whitening kit to anyone

I asked for a purrrrrfect rider!

That's why I've got a long neck

Berry, berry nice!

The new canine saddle!

Three heads are better...

This is soooo my best side

15

Duggie parle

16

Part 1
Français

DUGGIE

COLONEL

SOLOMAN

Say again?

I said *Bonjour*. It's French for good day.

I don't speak French.

He lets the funky music do the talking for him...

Don't tell me what I mean.

I can count in French. *Un... deux... trois...*

Don't you start!

Knew I wouldn't get to *quatre* before you got annoyed...

Can you both just STOP!

Do you mean *Arrêtez?*

Unbelieveable! That's it, I'm not talking to you until you cut out the French.

Can not talk to us, you mean...

Peut pas, I think!

HOW ANNOYING ARE DUGGIE AND THE COLONEL BEING? • WILL SOLOMAN GET REALLY NARKY? FIND OUT IN THE SECOND PART OF *DUGGIE PARLE FRANÇAIS*, ON PAGE 90.

COOL COBS!

The cob can be a recognised breed, or a type. Let's find out more!

COB TYPES

The Riding Cob

Cobs can be found all over the country. Generally speaking, a cob looks like a horse on shorter legs, and is stocky and well-rounded. A good cob should have a lot of bone (thickness of bone under the knee) to allow it to carry a lot of weight. Sometimes they are called weight-carrying cobs.

Show cobs are the creme-de-la-creme of the cob world – but even they are not specially bred. Most are discovered and, once trimmed and schooled, are transformed, like Cinderella! A good show cob has a leg at each corner and good conformation, and should be capable of galloping and jumping – they make great and safe hunters! There are even show classes for working cobs, which is a show class with natural jumps!

Show cobs can be of any colour and are always shown with hogged manes. There are two height classes at shows, cobs, and maxi cobs over 15.1hh.

THE COB OF WALES

The Welsh Cob is a specific breed, which means it breeds true to type, and has a recognised breed standard. There are two types – Welsh Cob Section C (up to 13.2hh) and Welsh Cob Section D (up to 15hh).

A gorgeous Welsh Cob

THE COB OF FRANCE

The Norman Cob is the cob of France! Valued for their all-round work nature, they are perfect for small farmers to use on Normandy smallholdings, and for small businesses who may want an all-round cob to ride and drive. They developed at the beginning of the 20th Century, when the French bred both riding horses and light draught horses.

The Norman Cob is heavier than the Welsh Cob, as it has been bred for farmwork. It looks much more like a small draught or heavy horse! It has only light feather on its heels and stands between 15.3hh and 16.2hh.

A cob line-up at a show

A show cob

Traditional Cobs

Coloured cobs which have long, flowing manes and tails and their leg feather left on are known as traditional cobs. These cobs are the traditional gypsy horses, and are often referred to as Gypsy Cobs, Romany Cobs, Vanners or Tinker's Cobs. They should be studily built, capable of being ridden or pulling a gypsy caravan, and be sound and good natured. Traditional Gypsy Cobs are shown untrimmed and unplaited, and have become very popular in recent years, changing hands for a lot of money.

DYK?

The ideal riding cob is traditionally supposed to have *the head of a lady's maid and the bottom of a cook!* From this you can see that cobs should be good looking, even though they are chunky, and proper work horses!

The traditional cob

GOT A COB?

Do you ride or own a cob? If you do, you'll know just how generous and gentle they can be – although they often possess a keen sense of humour! Cobs can literally be worth their weight in gold as they are a real all-round mount, and can be ridden by any member of the family – as well as turning their hooves to being driven!

PONY Magazine recommends that riders wear a correctly fastened, approved riding hat when riding.

Magic

PONY short story winner, by Laura Hampson

Join Emily for a thrilling ride around the cross country course at the world's toughest event - Badminton!

Emily tightened her grip on the reins, which were already becoming slack with sweat.

"Steady girl," she breathed to her horse. The mare shone like a roaring fire, her chestnut coat dancing like flickering flames, muscles rippling like a racehorse. Her tail cascaded behind her, flowing like a tumbling waterfall of flaxen hair. A snip sliced down her muzzle, as if someone had dipped their fingernail in a pot of white pain and placed it on her sooty nose. She stood at 15.3hh, a New Forest X. It was cross country day, and the mare was already tense, trembling with anticipation. She wanted to run.

As the steward approached them, he nodded at the girl. She was only young, 16 to be exact. This was her first time around Badminton, and she wanted it to be the best. The clock began the countdown, ticking off the seconds until the pair could start their round.

"Easy Magic, whoa," soothed Emily, in an attempt to soothe herself, if not her mount.

Five... four... The clock was ending its countdown.

Three... two... She gathered up the reins once more, preparing the mare for what was to come.

One!

The starting bell rang in Emily's ears, drowning out the cacophony of sound from both the huge crowd and the competitors.

"Ready when you are," the steward said to her. Emily crouched into a two-point position, and wrapped her legs around the mare's sturdy body. The starting box opened and Magic leapt out, like a racehorse springing from the starting gate.

She cantered ahead, locked onto the first jump, a narrow brush with a ditch underneath, there to test the rider's ability and horse's nerve. However scary the jump seemed, it didn't seem to faze the mare. Magic loved to jump, it was in her blood. Whenever she had the chance to do so, she would take it. Experienced and proficient, she advanced through the course like a walk around the park, still keeping a protective watch on the safety of her rider.

The course was one of those winding, twisty routes, with plenty of obstacles to test the ability of all. A competing horse needed the stamina and pace to make the way around the fences and the speed to keep within the optimum time. This year's course designer was determined to throw in any possible sticky situation to test the horse-and-rider partnership. Emily was the 17th competitor on course, and was determined to stay one-track minded, keeping her head in the game. Approaching fence number two, a wide tiger trap, she pushed on, willing to get the best out of her ride. Magic responded nicely, fitting in a long gallop to the jump.

> *Three... two... She gathered up the reins once more, preparing the mare for what was to come.*

She leapt over it, like an angel with wings as they flew to the other side, landing in line with the third jump. The pair continued to effortlessly soar over the obstacles, one at a time, working their way through a selection of arrowheads, tables, skinnies and airy oxers.

There were only two fences that frightened Emily, one of which they had already cleared. The other awaited their arrival. It had already tricked a lot of riders, laughing at them as they failed to clear it, accepting defeat from this giant monster. It lay on the ground, anticipating its next victim: The Vicarage Ditch.

Magic was going well – too well, if there was such a thing. She was now galloping flat out, still filled with energy and the excitement of cross country. Emily's cheeks were crimson in colour, the shade of ripe summer plums. They had completed over three-quarters of the course so far, but still to come was the final gruelling challenge. Thick sweat was beginning to foam around Magic's bit and it lapped around her neck. Emily patted her chestnut mare, flicking off some loose hairs with one long swipe. There were only seven obstacles left, and they were tackling them at an almighty speed. Over a spread, gallop, along a tight bend, turn, brush fence. The fences blurred past like a faded image on a crackling television screen. Four to go. The Vicarage Ditch was next.

It haunted riders, but Emily was determined not to be fooled by the tricky challenge. She knew Magic was capable of jumping it, and that was all she needed to know.

They cleared the arrowhead, turning into a dense clearing, surrounded by an army of trees, standing among each other like soldiers. The Vicarage Ditch came into view, its rolling wooden beams hung immaculately by the work of an artist. Flowers decorated the base of the jump as if to hide the width of the ditch underneath. It was more than a metre wide, and taller than the width.

Magic let out a snort, giving a toss of her head as if to say, "Don't worry about me, you know I can do this!"

Emily believed in her horse

and then she realised if they were going to do this, she needed to believe in herself. A partnership was never made full unless both believed they could do it. Magic believed in her, so she must follow her horse with that. Each ground-swallowing stride progressed them closer to the ditch. They had one minute left if they were to finish the course in the optimum time. Emily gathered her reins, asked with more leg and hoped. She could feel the mare lift, forelegs in the air, preparing to take to the massive jump. They were about to take off when suddenly, the horse's quarters dropped, pulling them down. Magic half-collapsed, bringing Emily down with a thud. She landed on the horse's neck, swinging to the side. Both her feet had come out of the stirrups and the mare's reins were dangling around her ears. They were only five strides out from the fence and the clock was still ticking.

Emily had a choice: she could either turn away from the fence and try again, clocking up time faults and a refusal, or she could try to get Magic up again, to carry on at the jump. Would she be able to gather the horse up ready to tackle the challenging ditch? If she tried, she could risk injuring herself and her horse. They had only five strides to get themselves together and Magic was still down on her knees.

> *Suddenly, the horse's quarters dropped, pulling them down. Magic half-collapsed, bringing Emily down with a thud*

Emily made her decision. It wasn't fair to make her horse struggle over the ditch from a standstill, she needed to turn around to try again. Tugging on her left rein, Emily sat back to let the horse regain her balance and stand

Posed by models

up. Then Magic changed her mind for her. She picked herself up, tilted her head as if to signal to her rider that she was ready, and charged towards the fence.

Emily grinned. It was typical of Magic, she always wanted to be the best, to prove that she was capable – and that was a lot. She lurched at the fence and Emily beamed a smile so big, she almost forgot what was to come. Magic galloped on, picking up speed like a Formula One racing car, accelerating towards the finish line. They were approaching the fence and this time, Emily was prepared for it. The chestnut mare arched over the fence, cresting it like a curvy moon. As they hit suspension, it was as though they were flying. Magic spread out her wings as they flew through the sky, in their own magical world. Her tail flicked out, whipping the air like a ringmaster's whip slicing the atmosphere. In a flurry of hoofbeats they landed on the other side, clearing the jump with room to spare.

> *In a flurry of hoofbeats they landed on the other side, clearing the jump with room to spare.*

Emily praised her horse like a queen, thanking her for taking the risk and getting herself ready. She could have stayed revelling in her glory of defeating the Vicarage Ditch, but right now she had a course to finish. Two jumps lay between them and the finish line, with only 40 seconds to complete them. Galloping on hard, the pair outwitted a combination of brushes, eyeing up the Trakehner, the final ditch. Surrounded by pink and yellow flowerpots, it was nothing like the humongous ditch they had just jumped. Emily gathered up her horse, looked for a stride and hoped with all her heart. They were clear so far and the Trakehner did nothing to change that. Magic and Emily had jumped a clear round, but they needed to cross the finish line before they ran out of time.

Twelve seconds... the clock was ticking. The girl pushed on, challenging the horse to go faster, fuelled with adrenaline, knowing they stood a chance. The line was in view, but they needed to carry on their charge if they were to make the optimum time.

Five... four... They were only 10 strides away from the finish and Emily was pushing harder, willing and asking the mare for more. Magic began to show signs of exhaustion, her heart was beating like thunder, sweat poured down her legs like dripping rain. They had three seconds and the two were so close, it was unbelievable. Driving on, Magic took one final stride, lengthening her pace so they could make it.

Two... she flew over the white painted line and the crowd cheered, a volcano erupting among the grandstands. One second to spare. Emily was shivering with excitement. How close they had come to missing the time! She hailed in glory, throwing her arms around Magic's neck, her mane scraggy from their mad gallop.

Running her hand down the horse's forehead, Emily buried her face among the mare's tangled forelock. "Come on then girl, let's get you back to the stables," She led Magic back to Badminton's famous barn, telling her horse how amazing she had been. Later that day, the scores were posted on the board from the cross country action, and Emily was overwhelmed to find that she and Magic were lying in fourth place, only two places behind Mary King! Straight away, she rushed over to tell Magic the news.

"Guess what girl? We're in fourth place so far, well done! You deserve lots of carrots and Polos after that round. Hence your name, girl, you really are *magic!*"

Riding double!

Riding with a friend? Try pairs riding!

Best mates

Before you team up with a riding buddy, make sure your ponies are chums. It's not only a drag trying to pair-ride with ponies who are trying to kick seven bells out of each other, but it's actually dangerous, so only ride in a pair if your ponies are best mates!

Choose your partner!

The best pairs riding happens when the ponies are similar in height, and have similar strides. Trying to ride your 14hh Highland with your mate on her 10hh Shetland isn't really a match made in heaven! You don't need to have matching ponies – although they look pretty swish, like our dun pair!

Make sure your ponies are friends!

Getting started

Start your pairs work in walk. Walk around the school, keeping together. Keep your ponies straight, so they don't bump into each other. Once you've walked two circuits of the school, change the rein across the diagonal, and go around on the other rein.

Stay as a pair – it's not easy!

Changing the rein

This is the tricky part. As you turn, the person riding on the outside needs to ask their pony to quicken the pace. The rider on the inside must ask their pony to shorten his stride, and slow down.

As you meet the opposite side, you will turn again – and this time the rider who was on the outside is now on the inside, and needs to go slower. The person who was on the inside needs to go faster – they're now on the outside!

You'll probably need some practise before you can change the rein without losing each other, but perfect pairs stay as a pair throughout the whole movement.

Circles

These are really tricky – and the closer you are together, the easier it is for the pony on the outside, who will need to get a wiggle on. The inside pony needs to do fairy steps to help out.

Experiment with school movements

You don't have to ride together all the time. You can experiment with riding at opposite sides of a circle (keeping the distance constant), and turning down the centre line, splitting up at A or C and then changing the rein across the diagonal to meet up again at X. Or how about getting really swish, and both performing a turn on the forehand at A or C – in opposite directions! See how many different school movements you can incorporate.

Taking it further

Why not put on a display for your friends? You can dress alike, and add matching ribbons in your ponies' manes and tails. Or why not look out for pairs classes at shows near you? They're great fun!

Pair riding will really improve your riding skills. How?

Test yourself by pairs jumping!

● You'll stop looking down at your pony, and be more aware of what's going on around you. This makes you ride instinctively, rather than over-concentrating on your pony.

● **Changes of rein require a change of pace. It's perfect for teaching your pony to shorten and lengthen his stride, or to listen to your requests for him to slow down and speed up.**

● Talk to your friend so that you both work together. One of you shouldn't be in charge – it's a partnership.

● **As you try to ride as a pair, get your knees level, rather than concentrating on your pony's heads. This looks much better to anyone watching you. You'll become much more spatially aware.**

● Experiment with different patterns and movements. If you're really good, you'll progress to jumping as a pair!

● **You can practise your pairs riding out hacking!**

23

Make some pony artwork!

You will need:

- Simple horse designs
- A picture frame (we found ours in a charity shop)
- An old book (a charity shop find again!)
- Coloured card
- Paste
- Scissors

1 First, find an image you would like to reproduce. A very simple design is best. There are three designs here to choose from – just scan them, enlarge them and print them out on your computer – or find another you like.

2 For the three horses, cut around the whole outline carefully. Then trace them onto coloured card and cut around again. You will have all three horses.

The enlarged scan

Cut them out of cardboard

3 Now cut the third horse away from the others and repeat the procedure so you have two horses in another colour.

Repeat with all three outlines

24

4
Cut the second horse away and repeat the above so you have the third horse in another colour.

5
Now carefully paste all three horses together so they look like the original design.

All three colours together

6
From an old book, cut out some pages and paste them as a background in your frame. Centre your coloured horses and fix them firmly.

There! One fab modern artwork!

Why not try another design?

The finished design!

Which design will you choose?

Fashion disaster!

Real Life!
Being nice to ♡ Mrs Tingle

How could Isabel ever compete if she didn't have her own pony?

Mrs Tingle was a sweet old lady who kept her pony at the riding school. Merlin was a dark bay, ordinary sort of pony, and he plodded along quite happily with Mrs Tingle on board. I liked Mrs Tingle, she was always so lovely to Merlin, but my friend Angie wasn't so keen.

"She's ancient," she'd say, whenever we saw Mrs Tingle ambling off down the bridlepath. "She must be in her 50s. She can't really control Merlin. Look, he's snatching at the branches as they go along!"

"Oh leave them alone," I replied. "She's not hurting anyone, and Merlin looks after her. If it doesn't bother him, why should it bother you?" And I'd be extra nice to Mrs Tingle, to try and make up for Angie's attitude. It was really nothing to do with Angie, I thought, as I asked Mrs Tingle how Merlin was today, and offered to help her pick out his hind hooves.

"Thank you Isabel, that's very kind of you," Mrs Tingle would say. "Merlin likes you!" And I'd give Merlin a pat.

NO PONIES OF OUR OWN

Angie and I didn't have our own ponies, but we helped at the riding school, and rode our favourites. Julie, who ran the school, said we were her favourite helpers, and we were often called to ride a pony who might be playing up with a novice rider, or show someone how to put a bridle on Sam, who always put his head up out of reach. We *wanted* our own ponies, but we were still learning a lot at the riding school. The only time I felt left out was when there was a competition on – and the school organised them regularly. It was a few weeks before Easter when we saw the notice.
Hunter Trials Easter Saturday.
Three classes – Horses, Ponies and Open.
It would be held on the school's own cross country course – solid, but not very big – and was open to liveries and other, privately-owned horses and ponies in the area. Not the school horses, of course. They had to work on Saturdays.

"Oh I wish I could take Opel around that!" wailed Angie, talking about her favourite school pony who could jump like a stag. I longed to try it, too. But there was no way it was going to happen. But sometimes, you know, things surprise you.

A BIG SURPRISE

Merlin was in one of his *my-feet-can't-leave-the-ground* moods when I walked into the yard one morning. I went over to help the puffing Mrs Tingle, and soon Merlin's hooves were clean.

"He is a naughty boy!" scolded Mrs Tingle, patting Merlin's neck in an adoring fashion. "I'm glad I've seen you, Isabel," she continued. "I wanted to ask you something."

"Oh yes?" I said, without a clue what was coming.

"Would you like to ride Merlin in the Hunter Trial?"

I think my mouth dropped open like a goldfish. I hadn't seen that coming!

"Oh yes please!" I cried, hugging Mrs Tingle. She looked quite pleased. But then I wondered about Merlin. Did he even know how to jump? It was as though Mrs Tingle could read my mind.

"He hasn't done it for ages, of course, but my Merlin used to be quite a good Pony Club pony. I sometimes think he's wasted on me, but maybe he'll enjoy reliving his glory days," she said.

Angie was sceptical, but after I'd had a few practices, at Mrs Tingle's insistence, she soon changed her mind.

"Wow Izz, he can jump all right!" she said, as Merlin flew over the jumps in the school.

LIVING MY DREAM

On the day of the Hunter Trial, I groomed Merlin until he shone – I was determind Mrs Tingle would be proud of us, whatever the outcome. And when I walked him around before the start, she looked so excited, I realised it was thrilling for us both. I could hardly believe I was competing on Merlin. I felt like Mary King!

Our round was fantastic! Merlin wasn't the fastest pony, but he was a careful jumper and he looked after me. When we came through the finish line I thought I would burst, and I think Mrs Tingle felt the same. We came fourth in the pony class, and Mrs Tingle looked so proud, I was as happy for her as I was for myself.

PONY CLUB CAMP!

That wasn't the last time I rode Merlin. Mrs Tingle can't always get to the yard, so I ride him twice a week – and this year she wants me to take him to Pony Club camp. I'm so glad I was nice to Mrs Tingle!

Merlin wasn't the fastest pony, but he was a careful jumper...

posed by models

27

What ponies think about Food

Ever wondered what your fave pony thinks about? Here's our take on it – with some pretty helpful tips to further your relationship!

Ponies think about eating ALL THE TIME! Why? Because they have small stomachs. Because they have evolved over millions of years to eat tiny amounts of grass and forage to trickle through their digestive system practically 24/7. We eat three meals a day (and possibly some snacks!) and feel full afterwards, but ponies, with their small stomachs, can't do this. Little and often is the mantra when feeding ponies. That's why your pony tries to snack when you're out riding!

We try to replicate this way of eating by feeding small feeds, and giving hay when our ponies are stabled, as bulk to replace grass. The best way to keep ponies, and the most natural, is for them to graze in a field day and night. The only exception to this are ponies which suffer from being overweight, and those prone to laminitis. Even so, fitting a grazing muzzle is a good way to allow your pony to wander around the field, exercising himself, munching tiny amounts.

Other ponies: one

Ponies are herd animals. They love to be surrounded by their mates. This is because a: they *like* their mates, and b: they know that in the wild, being part of a group means they're less likely to be picked off by that wolf or lion prowling about. It's a bit mercenary when you think about it – rather you than me – but it certainly helps to have a lot of chums around to confuse the enemy, rather than being on your own.

And, of course, the more eyes and ears around to notice predators, the better!

Other ponies: two

Not all ponies are buddies. Some are more dominant than others. Some are a bit shy and retiring. Others are somewhere in between – nervous of the dominant ponies, and bossy with the others. This makes the dynamics of a field full of ponies an explosive place.

They will always sort themselves out into a pecking order, but you need to understand that order so you don't get into trouble. Leading a lower-ranking pony past a dominant one in the gateway, for example, can lead to a fight. The dominant pony will try to put the lower pony in its place – and you stand a chance of getting caught in the middle.

Also, if your pony is stabled in a barn, with other ponies either side who can pull faces at him, he can become miserable. Imagine sitting next to someone at school who constantly bullies you. Not nice. So it's a good idea to find out how your pony feels about his neighbours, and take steps to ensure he feels safe and secure in his surroundings. Otherwise, he'll suffer from stress.

Sleep

Ponies don't sleep like we do. Instead of a big sleep during the night, they tend to take lots of naps, usually standing up. After all, they need to keep re-fuelling, remember? (See food)

Having lots of naps means your pony may doze off on lessons when you're standing about, or get a few zeds in when he's being groomed. This isn't a problem, until you want him to do something on said lesson (give him a moment to gather his thoughts, not to mention his legs), or something startling happens in the yard or stable while he's not quite awake. It's just a good thing to be aware of, that's all.

Work

You may think your pony doesn't think about his work, but his brain will be processing data from schooling and lessons, even without him being aware of it. That's why it's important always to end a lesson or schooling session on a good note, when your pony had done well. Even if he hasn't quite understood what you want him to do, never overdo it. Always make lessons short.

You will find, after an evening off, your pony will come back the next day and will remember more than you ever imagined. He may even surprise you by doing what you want first time! But don't take our word for it – try it out!

FACT OR FICTION?

There are plenty of old wives' tales about horses and ponies – but are they all just that, or is there any truth in them? See how many you can get right!

1 Ponies grow their winter coats when the weather turns colder.

○ True ○ False

2 White hooves are weaker than black ones.

○ True ○ False

3 Horses can't be sick.

○ True ○ False

4 Ponies who gallop towards jumps love jumping!

○ True ○ False

5 Chestnut mares are temperamental nutcases!

○ True ○ False

30

6
There is no such thing as a white horse, they're all grey.

- ○ True
- ● False

7
Horses can't breathe through their mouths.

- ○ True
- ● False

8
You shouldn't let a pony with colic lie down.

- ○ True
- ● False

9
Too much grass causes laminitis.

- ○ True ○ False

10
A horse can grow a whole new hoof in a year.

- ○ True ● False

LET'S FIND OUT WHICH ARE TRUE AND WHICH ARE FALSE!

1. False. It is the hours of daylight that triggers a pony's hair growth, not temperature. In spring, when the days start to get longer, ponies shed their winter coats and grow their summer ones. When the days shorten in the autumn, they grow their winter coats in earnest. It's not about temperature, but daylight hours.

2. This is a very long-standing belief, and even has a verse to reinforce it. Have you heard it? *One white foot, buy a horse, two white feet, try a horse. Three white feet, look well about him, four white feet, do without him!* There is no difference in the structure, density or moisture content between white and dark hooves, so there is no difference in strength. Strength of hooves relies on a high moisture content, not colour.
It could be the rhyme is about leg colour – and there is evidence to suggest that white legs suffer more from complaints like mud fever.

3. True. Horses have a one-way valve that blocks the entrance from the oesophagus (food tube) to the stomach. Food can go down, but it can't come back up. This is why colic is so serious. If we feel ill we can be sick and get rid of what's making us feel bad. Horses can't.

4. False. They want to get it over with as quickly as possible! Most ponies rush their jumps because they are anxious, confused, in pain or inexperienced. There may be a physical problem – and poorly-fitted tack and bad riding can cause rushing.

5. False. This is a myth. It's true that mares in general can be more sensitive than geldings, particularly when in season, but it has nothing to do with colour. However, research on humans show evidence that red-heads do have a lower pain threshold and are more sensitive – could the same apply to horses? Perhaps. As yet, however, it is unproven.

6. False. Grey horses have black skin and are born black or chestnut. Cremello and perlino horses are not white, either. However, a horse which is white all over with pink skin is a white horse – but these are very, very rare.

7. True. They breathe through their nostrils. A flap of tissue called the soft palate blocks the pharynx (breathing tube) from the mouth to stop the horse inhaling food.

8. False. It used to be thought that it was best to walk colic cases, and not to allow them to lie down. However, vets now say that as long as the horse or pony lies quietly, and does not thrash around, it is safe to let him lie down. (Always call the vet if your pony has colic!)

9. False. It is the high levels of fructans (sugar) in grass that cause laminitis. It is currently believed that fresh, spring grass is high in fructans, as is grass that has recently been frosty. This type of grass is more likely to cause laminitis.

10. True. Healthy hooves grow at a rate of about one centimetre a month.

SO NOW YOU KNOW!

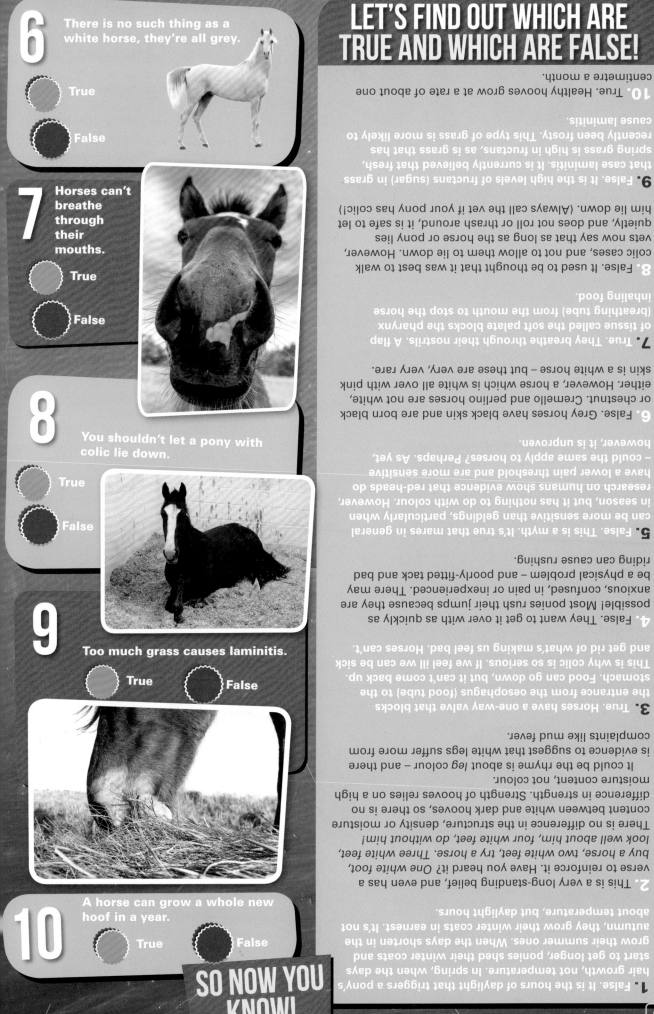

Perfect position!

How's your riding position? Finding it tricky to keep it? Feel a bit wobbly? Don't know how to correct it? Read on for positional advice that really works!

Heads up!

You'd be surprised how many riders look down – and it looks terrible! Not only that, it shifts your weight in the saddle, prevents you from looking where you are going, and slows your pony down – yes, really!

It's an easy thing to correct. Just look up! Look where you are going. You don't need to look at your pony – learn to *feel* what is going on under you. If you do want to look down, you can do it without dropping your chin into your neck – just lower your eyes! And remember to keep your ears level, no dipping one side of your head so you're lopsided. Your pony will think you want to turn that way!

Top head tip

To keep your head in the right place, imagine someone pulling a string at the very top of your head – like a marionette! Or pretend to be a very snooty rider – stick that nose in the air and keep it there! You can *look* down – but don't drop your chin!

That's handy!

Everyone has problems with their hands and rein contact at some point in their riding career. The most important things to remember are that your hands need to work as a pair – so don't let one hand go up while the other one drops – and your rein contact is your line of communication with your pony. It should be light, yet constant, so your hands need to move backwards and forwards with his head and neck movements. Carry your own hands above his withers. If you rest them on your pony's neck, how can you use them?

Top rein tip

Holding your stick between your thumbs and your reins will have a miraculous effect on your hands – and the way your pony goes. Try it!

Body talk!

When you look at good riders, their bodies never seem to move, do they? It's as though they're stuck with glue! But to look like that, the rider needs to be supple through the back, and move their hips in time with their horse's hips. So really, they're not sitting still at all. The secret is not to move your *shoulders*. Keep your shoulders still and move your *hips* along with your pony – especially in canter. Then it will look as though you are sitting as still as those riders you admire!

Top body tip

Keep your back supple to allow for movement in your hips. The more stiff you are, the more you will bounce about – like a wooden clothes peg!

Lucky legs!

Ahhh, legs – so much can go wrong. Either your legs are too far back, or too far forward, or your heels are digging into your pony, or your knees are sticking out. Phew! The way to get your legs right is to think of them as cooked pieces of spaghetti. They'd drop naturally down, wouldn't they, on either side of your pony? They wouldn't be stiff, or move about – and they'd be close to your pony's sides, too.

Keep your toes pointing to the front (not out to the side), and the weight in your heels. Don't *push* your heels down, that will just make your legs go stiff and force your legs to go too far forward. Our model could have her lower leg back a little and a more relaxed ankle to be ideal.

Top leg tips

Use your legs inwards, not backwards. Your pony is more sensitive near his girth, so use your legs there. Imagine your pony is a balloon, and you need to straddle it without popping it!

Forward position

For jumping or riding across country, the forward seat is adopted. Shorten your stirrups two – three holes and, keeping your knees and ankles soft and supple, and your legs underneath you, shorten your reins and rise out of the saddle to take your weight off your pony's back.

This technique requires some practice, so why not have a few sessions a week at canter? Keep to a straight line until you feel secure!

FILL IN THE BLANKS!

How well do you know the points of a horse – and the parts of a saddle and bridle? See how many you can fill in.

POINTS OF THE HORSE

Can you name all the points we've indicated here? Some are easy – but others are quite tricky!

1 ....
2 ....
3 ....
4 ....
5 ....
6 ....
7 ....
8 ....
38 ....
39 ....
40 ....
41 ....
37 ....
36 ....
35 ....
34 ....
33 ....
32 ....
31 ....
30 ....
29 ....
28 ....
27 ....
26 ....
25 ....
24 ....
23 ....
22 ....
21 ....
20 ....
19 ....

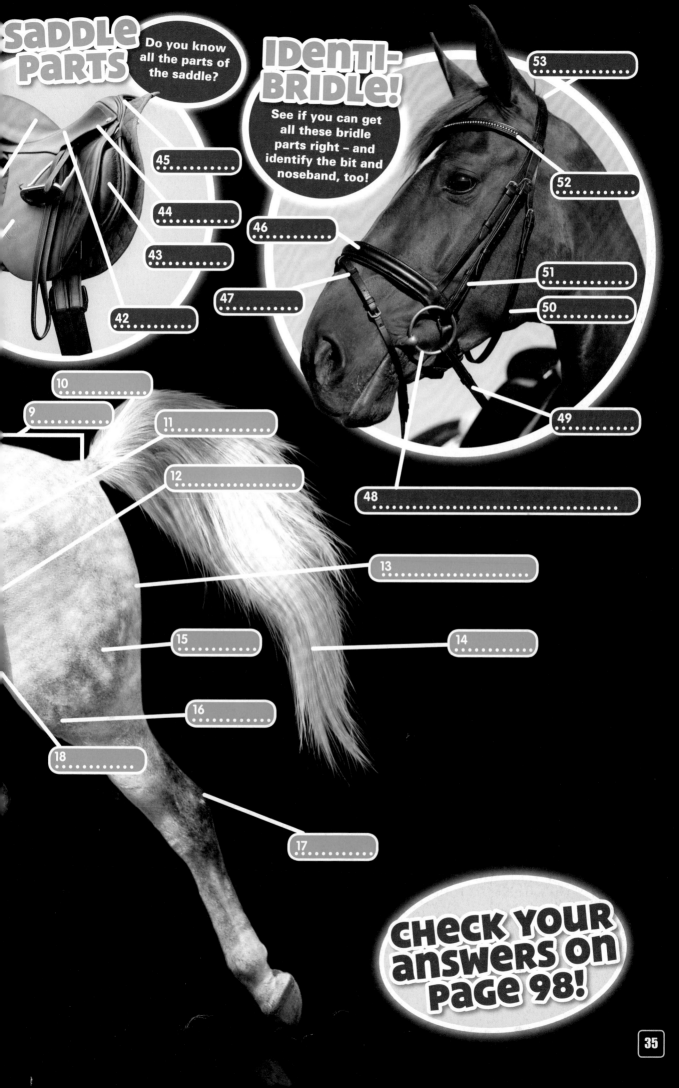

SADDLE PARTS

Do you know all the parts of the saddle?

45 ....

44 ....

43 ....

42 ....

IDENTI-BRIDLE!

See if you can get all these bridle parts right – and identify the bit and noseband, too!

53 ....

52 ....

51 ....

50 ....

46 ....

47 ....

49 ....

48 ....

10 ....

9 ....

11 ....

12 ....

13 ....

15 ....

14 ....

16 ....

18 ....

17 ....

CHECK YOUR ANSWERS ON PAGE 98!

11 ways to improve your jumping!

Jump like a pro with our ideas to make your jumping more successful!

1 Don't neglect the basics

It's no good aiming for the jumps if you and your pony can't even turn corners in a balanced way. Flatwork will improve your jumping, so it's vital to pay attention and really work on it!

2 Build your confidence – and your pony's!

It's natural to want to jump higher and higher, but being able to tackle the lower jumps well will give you and your pony confidence to progress. Never overface yourselves or take a chance.

3 Learn from your mistakes

When things go wrong (and they will), it isn't the end of the world. It's an opportunity to assess what went wrong so you don't do it again! Nobody ever got to the top without making mistakes, so you're in good company. Just don't waste them!

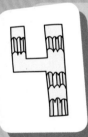

4 Enter competitions

Don't wait until you're soaring over five-bar gates before entering the clear round jumping at your local show. You and your pony need to get used to jumping different fences in a competitive situation. It's very different to jumping at home, so practice at the small shows and work your way up.

5 Know when to stop schooling

Schooling sesh going brilliantly? Tempted to try just one more jump, just a little bigger? Slow down! Why risk blowing that great session? Always end on a good note before you and your pony get tired. Your pony will remember and be keen next time!

Improve your style

Having regular jumping lessons will help your technique and hone your skills. Sure, some sloppy riders are successful – but the very best have great jumping style. Work on yours!

Ride with your brain!

Be an intelligent jumper. Work out how to approach different types of jumps so your pony can jump them easily. Walk the course and plan your route. Be the brains behind you and your pony's partnership!

Respect your pony

Ponies aren't machines and sometimes they have off-days or are reluctant to jump. Respect your pony – he's your partner, not your slave. He may have a very good reason for his behaviour.

Hurry slowly

If things start to go wrong, take a step back or change your routine. Go for a hack, leave the jumping for a day or so, or even a week. There's plenty of time to be the next Jess Mendoza, so take your time and have a break.

Hone your skills

Don't just be content to jump – try to be the very best at jumping! Ride different ponies and try different things to make sure your jumping skills are constantly being challenged – and they'll improve!

Enjoy yourself!

We're supposed to enjoy riding so make sure you (and your pony) do just that. Try not to get too intense – have a laugh now and again!

Time for a pony relationship makeover!

If you think your relationship with your pony could do with an overhaul, we've got some ideas right here!

Mean only good things to your pony

We all love people who make us feel good – and ponies are no exception. They don't like people who moan, or nag, or make them do boring, repetitive things like jumping, over and over again when they're tired or bored.

They do like people who are enthusiastic, who praise them when they do well (instead of always telling them off), and thinking up interesting things to do. Are you that person? If not, can you become that person? Of course you can!

Put your pony first

Real horsemen and women always care for their horses before they care for themselves. And horses appreciate it. So go the extra mile. Do you make sure your pony is well groomed before you ride? Is his tack always clean and therefore comfortable for him to wear? Does he have a deep bed, a full haynet and clean water at all times? Do you turn him out to play with his mates – even when it's muddy? Is he booked in regularly for the farrier, the equine dentist and for his vaccinations, and has he a regular worming programme?

All these things contribute to your pony's health, and when he's healthy, he's happy, and when he's happy, he'll have more time for you – because you're the one making him happy!

Notice things

Your relationship with your pony will improve greatly if you notice things he likes, and make sure you do things for him! Some ponies love having their ears pulled gently. Others enjoy a strong scratch with a rubber curry comb to loosen any old coat which is due to be shed. Some ponies enjoy you singing to them, and others enjoy using their brains, and seeking out apples and carrots buried in their beds!

Find out what your pony likes – so you can do it for him. That way, he'll look forward to your visits and reward you with a whinny when you arrive at the yard!

Be fair

Ponies like to know where they stand, and they enjoy consistancy in a relationship. Make sure you don't tell your pony off for doing something one day, then laugh at the same behaviour the next. He'll not only be confused, he'll think you're weird – not to mention unreasonable.

Set clear boundaries, and expect your requests to be met. If they are not, be certain you are asking in a clear way, and stand firm. Your relationship needs to be based on respect, so expect respect from your pony. In return, make sure you give him respect back. Respect him for being a pony (and only expect pony behaviour from him!), and ensure your relationship is a two-way one.

Hurry slowly - and seek help

If you are trying hard to build your relationship with your pony, don't expect it to be revolutionalised overnight. Progress slowly, with patience and love, and you'll see results over time. If after a while you feel you're getting nowhere, don't be too proud to ask for help from your instructor, or a knowledgeable person who you feel has a good relationship with their horse or pony. They'll be only too happy to help you!

Know your pony

Does your pony like to go first or last on a ride? Which ponies does he get on with, and which does he dislike? What are his favourite routes out hacking, and which competitions does he enjoy? Forcing your pony to ride with ponies who bully him, or entering jumping competitions when he clearly enjoys dressage is not the pathway to a great relationship!

Tony's Ponies

Could two rival stable owners ever put their differences behind them and become friends?

PONY short story winner, by Cara Padden
Illustrated by the author

On the outskirts of a small village in the South of Ireland there were two riding academies. One was called Golden Hoof Riding Academy, owned by Amber, and the other was called Tony's Ponies – owned by Tony! They were both very good at different things. They competed in lots of different competitions together, and sometimes Tony's Ponies would win, and sometimes Golden Hoof Riding Academy would win.

One day, Golden Hoof Riding Academy got a new pony called Buttons. He could jump so high, and could hunt so well, he was perfect. Soon, Buttons won every competition he went to. Tony soon started to grow jealous, and he grew so jealous, he thought of a plan to make Buttons his own.

You see, Tony had a pony called Popping Candy, and he looked exactly like Buttons. It was as though they were twins. Tony decided he would steal Buttons away and replace him at Golden Hoof Riding Academy with Popping Candy! That night Fred, who worked at Tony's Ponies, and Tony, crept out with Popping Candy. When they got to Golden Hoof Riding Academy, they found Buttons in his stable, drinking from his water bucket.

"Fred," said Tony, "take Buttons out and get Popping Candy into Buttons' stable."

"He's a lovely pony, isn't he?" said Fred.

"Yes he is," replied Tony.

They crept back down the road, back to Tony's Ponies with Buttons, and put him in Popping Candy's loosebox.

In the morning at Golden Hoof Riding Academy, Popping Candy was saddled up and ridden on a lesson by Máire. Soon, it was time for some jumping. That, of course, wouldn't be a problem for Buttons. However, it wasn't Buttons on the lesson, it was Popping Candy. And the thing about Popping Candy was that he had never even seen a jump in his life!

As soon as Amber looked at Popping Candy, she knew it wasn't Buttons – and she also knew where Buttons was... Amber and Máire ran down the road with Popping Candy until they got to Tony's Ponies. Tony was loading Buttons into the horsebox when they got there.

"Tony!" shouted Amber. "You stole my pony, didn't you? Come on, just admit it!"

"Oh all right," said Tony, "I admit I stole Buttons. But I only did it because I was so jealous of how good Buttons is. I am truly sorry," Tony lied.

"Really?" asked Amber.

> Both stables were good at different things

"No," whispered Tony.

"Are you going to call the guards?" asked Fred.

"No," replied Máire, "just give us back Buttons and we'll give you Popping Candy."

"But..." shrieked Tony.

"No buts," warned Máire.

"Oh, fine!" Tony agreed, and he handed Buttons back to Máire while Amber gave Popping Candy back to Fred.

The girls walked Buttons back along the road, fussing over him and telling him how glad they were that he was back. They finally got back to Golden Hoof Riding Academy, and Buttons was reunited with all his friends, who were also very glad to see him again.

Meanwhile, at Tony's Ponies, Tony was very frustrated at how his plan had failed. And when Tony got upset or frustrated, he tended to smoke, even though everyone knows you should never smoke – and you should certainly never, ever smoke near a stables. And when Tony got upset or frustrated and started to smoke, he got careless, and one of his matches, which he thought was out, wasn't, and it smouldered in the hay. And as Tony drove home the hay caught alight, and started a fire at Tony's Ponies.

Back at Golden Hoof Riding Academy, Amber was just on her last check on all the horses for the night when she looked across the fields towards Tony's Ponies, and saw that the stables were on fire! Amber raced down to Tony's Ponies. First she got out all the horses. Next she put out the fire with a fire extinguisher and when the fire was finally out, Amber called Tony and told him what had happened. While Tony was on his way back, Amber checked to see if any of the horses were hurt but fortunately, none of them were. Finally, Tony arrived at the yard, and couldn't have been more grateful to Amber for saving his stables.

From that day on, Amber and Tony became the very best of friends!

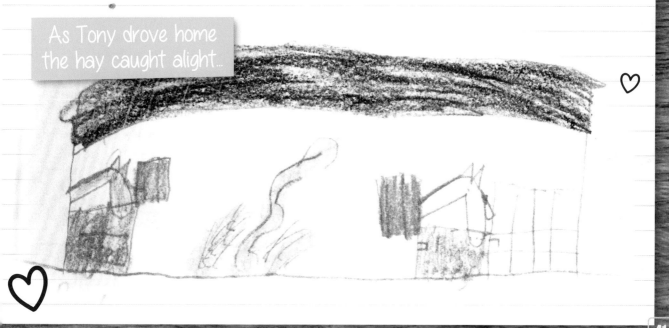

HAPPY HACKING!

Open spaces

There is nothing quite as exhilarating as galloping across an open field, but it is still important to stay in control of your pony. Ponies who are up for a good gallop are great fun, but they need to slow down and stop when you ask them to. If you're not sure how the pony you're riding will react, start with long trots or controlled canters in very open spaces before galloping. Practice transitions in the school and on hacks so your pony is clear that when you ask him to stop, he needs to do so.

Hacking with a friend on a very sensible pony can help, too, just make sure the ponies don't start racing!

A good gallop is great fun...

...but being out-of-control isn't!

Gates

Gates are common out hacking and knowing how to open and close them while mounted makes them a whole lot easier!

Approach the gate and ask your pony to stand still, parallel to the gate and close to it. Use your hand nearest to the gate to unfasten the latch, then either pull or push the gate open and pass through. To close the gate behind you, turn your pony around and either pull or push the gate shut. Ask him again to stand still and parallel to the gate while you refasten the latch.

It all sounds simple but opening and closing gates efficiently can take some practice, especially with young ponies.

Practice makes perfect with gates

Making a splash!

Water

Some ponies love water and others take quite a dislike to getting their feet wet! Out hacking you might need to ride through streams, and in wet weather, large puddles! Ponies that are keen on water might have a splash around, but if he starts pawing at the water, move him on pretty swiftly as it could be a sign that he's thinking about rolling!

Ponies that are water-shy will need some gentle encouragement so they can build their confidence. Hacking out with a pony who will happily go through water will help as they can give a not-so-keen pony a lead. Always walk nervous ponies through water so a minimal amount of splash is created.

All pictures posed by models

Hills

Hills are great for both cross country practice and for getting ponies fit, but they can be tricky to ride.

Uphill slopes require riders to keep their leg on as it is easier for ponies to get up hills if they are moving forward. Also, adopting a slightly forward seat will help you stay in balance with your pony.

Riding downhill needs control and good balance. Lean back slightly to stay in balance. Leaning forward will put your weight onto the forehand and could make your pony unsteady and unbalanced.

If your pony has a tendency to rush down hills, lean back a little more than you would on a pony who doesn't rush, and keep the walk as slow as possible. Give him confidence by staying in balance and encourage him to take it steady!

Hills are great for fittening work

Be seen on the roads

Roads

It is best to avoid riding on roads where you can, but sometimes it is necessary to get where you're going! Hi-viz gear is essential so you can be easily seen by traffic. Also, make sure you know the Highway Code before riding on the road so you ride safely, and know your signals to traffic. Respect other road users and be aware of traffic at all times. Some cars are very quiet and you and your pony may not hear them coming!

Young or nervous ponies may be more skittish on the road, so make sure to slow traffic down to give your pony plenty of time to see what's coming.

Ditches and logs

You may come across ditches or logs to jump out hacking, and sometimes there isn't a way around them. They can be great cross country practice, but need to be tackled with some care. Make sure you assess the ditch or jump carefully before jumping it! Ask yourself: Is the ground either side of the ditch safe and suitable? Is the ditch or log too big for my pony to manage? Is there a way around the jump which is safer than jumping it?

If you do have to jump a ditch, approach in trot rather than canter to allow your pony to look at what you're asking him to jump. Some ponies find ditches scary!

Combining hacking and jumping!

Other people and animals

It is likely that you will encounter walkers, cyclists, dogs and other horses when out hacking.

Ask dog walkers to put their dogs on a lead if they are loose. Even if your pony is used to dogs and the dog is used to ponies, it is safest to keep them on a lead until you have passed by, particularly so if your pony is nervous of dogs.

Some ponies may get excited to see another horse out hacking, so it is best to pass by with minimal fuss.

Cyclists can be very quiet or appear suddenly so could give your pony a bit of a shock if he is surprised by one! Don't be too shy to ask cyclists to stop so you can pass by if your pony is upset by them!

"Fancy seeing you here!"

Hacking in a group

Hacking out with your mates is great fun for you and your pony! Depending on the size of the group, you might ride side-by-side or in single file. It is important to keep in mind whether any of the ponies in the group dislike each other, or if one is bullied by another, as riding these ponies next to each other could make for an eventful and stressful ride – for you and your pony!

Some ponies get much more excitable in company, whereas others are calmed by the influence of sensible ponies, and some like to be at the front of the ride while others are happier at the back! Make sure you know your pony and what he's likely to behave like in company.

Grab your mates and hit the bridlepaths!

Elegant Hacks

Like the riding cob, a hack is a type of horse, not a breed.

What's a hack?

A hack is, technically, any horse which is used for hacking. Show hacks are Thoroughbred horses, elegant, refined, well mannered and schooled to the highest standard. A show hack should be able to be ridden with the reins in one hand.

Historic hacks

It used to be very fashionable to ride one's hack up and down Rotten Row in London, to be seen by society. Naturally, the horse needed to be eye-catching as well as being beautifully schooled. Both women and men would ride, and a lady's show hack today is ridden side saddle. A lady's hack in yesteryear would be trained always to lead with the offside near fore in canter, as that was most comfortable for its rider.

An historic side saddle habit

Dyk?

There used to be two types of hack: the *park* hack and the *covert* hack. Park hacks were ridden around the parks of cities by people of society in order to meet each other and take exercise. The slightly heavier covert hacks were ridden to hunt meets, and the rider would then swap to their hunter!

A beautiful show hack

Hack requirements

Most show hacks are Thoroughbreds or Anglo-Arabs, but although they must be elegant and graceful, they must still have good bone and substance. Show hacks are not required to gallop in the show ring, but their individual display must demonstrate their schooling and good manners.

Show hacks sport decorated quarters!

Dyk?

The word hack is from the Norman French word *haquenée*, which meant a light riding horse.

Dressing the part

There are many rules and regulations governing showing and show dress for riders of hacks. Gentlemen at the evening and royal shows wear a traditional tailcoat with a waistcoat and top hat. Women riders astride wear traditional dress, but in evening and royal classes, can wear a top hat and a stock. Hacks are always shown with a coloured browband, and their riders may wear a matching buttonhole in their lapel.

Next time you go to a show, see whether there are any hack classes to watch and - try to judge which one will win!

Horse and rider in matching outfits!

How to get the tidiest yard

A tidy yard equals a tidy mind, right? Or at least peace of mind knowing the yard is a happy and safe place for your pony to live! Check out our top tidying tips!

DANGER ON THE YARD?

A messy yard can be a dangerous place. There are lots of potential hazards when people are careless with their equipment or lazy with their yard chores. Take a look at this pic and see if you can spot the hazards:

TURN TO PAGE 98 FOR THE ANSWERS!

HOW MANY DID YOU GET?

0-3 correct
Oh dear, you're clearly not aware of yard hazards. Try to be more cautious and consider potential hazards, rather than being too relaxed and risking an accident!

4-6 correct
You're pretty safety savvy and like a tidy yard but you could still be more hazard-concious. Look around the yard every time you leave or go out for a ride and make sure everything is in order.

7-10 correct
Well done! You're clearly aware of the hazards of a messy yard and work hard to keep yours tidy and safe. Keep up the good work!

What should be in order and why?

A safe yard where things can be found quickly and easily is essential. Check out this list to see if your yard is as tidy as it could be!

Anyone lost a brush?

Stables

Stables should be clean and neat with a bedding material suitable for each pony. Deep beds are ideal and they are comfier for the pony and easier on his legs.

Mucking out (or skipping out if your pony is on deep litter) each day is essential. Your pony won't appreciate a dirty or messy bedroom!

The yard itself

It's easy to leave things lying around the yard, like the odd brush or poo scoop. But not only is this a good way to lose your things, it can be dangerous if a pony (or person!) treads or trips on it. Plus, if everyone did it the yard would be a right mess! Take time to pick up any equipment you've used and return it to it's home.

Sweeping the yard regularly is important, too. Loose hay and straw, as well as dirt and mud from hooves, are the most common mess-makers and it all accumulates quickly. So get to grips with the yard broom, pronto!

Watchpoint!

BE ORGANISED WITH YOUR YARD DUTIES AND GET INTO A ROUTINE THAT WORKS. IT CAN BE HELPFUL TO MAKE A LIST OF THINGS THAT NEED TO BE DONE DAILY, WEEKLY AND MONTHLY, SO YOU STAY ON TOP OF EVERYTHING!

Tack room

A messy tack room can be a nightmare, as not knowing for sure whose tack is whose can cause all sorts of problems! An ideal tack room will have separate bridle pegs and saddle stands for each pony, and will be clearly labelled.

Other items of tack and numnahs and saddlecloths should be stored neatly and in such a way that it's clear which belongs to which pony.

A neat and tidy tack room!

Feed room

It is important that everyone at the yard knows which feed each pony has so they don't get fed the wrong thing! Keeping a whiteboard or a chart that everyone can see with each pony's feed details on can be helpful – especially if you have help or a sharer who sometimes feeds your pony for you.

Make sure bins are clearly labelled with the feed inside, and ensure product names on bags are visible so it is always clear what each feed is. The same goes for any supplements.

Storing feed in metal or plastic bins is ideal because they are airtight, and rats and mice can't get to them, whereas they can easily gnaw through feeds bags! Also, make sure to sweep up any feed dropped on the floor, as this will also attract pests.

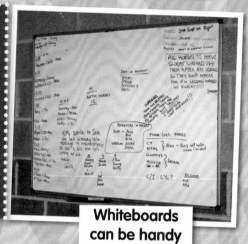

Whiteboards can be handy

A shining example!

The muck heap

Keeping the yard muck heap in order is important, as it is easy to let it spread out, and is very hard work to get back in order once it's messy. Everyone in the yard should contribute to keeping the muck heap tidy.

Empty your wheelbarrow as near to the back of the heap as possible and if need be, throw manure to the top with your fork.

Watchpoint!

DON'T FORGET TO HAVE A GOOD SPRING CLEAN ONCE A YEAR TO SORT OUT ITEMS YOU NO LONGER USE OR NEED. IT WILL HELP YOU CLEAR SPACE AND MAKE IT EASIER TO KEEP THINGS TIDY!

Medical kit

Some yards, particularly riding schools, have a communal medical kit that can be used in emergencies. The first important thing is that everyone knows where it is kept and can access it quickly. Also, someone should be responsible for checking all the products are in date, as some have expiry dates and should not be used after the date has passed.

Remember to replace anything you use, so that the kit is always fully stocked, and make sure everything is easy to find and labelled correctly.

Tools

Tools are safest and easiest to access when they are hung up on pegs. It also means someone needing to use a tool can clearly see what is available without rooting through a cupboard, for example, and risking breaking something or hurting themselves.

You will be more inclined to put tools back if it is as easy as hooking them onto a peg!

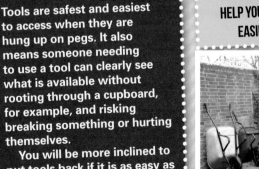

Beautifully displayed tools!

PONY FRIENDS OR FOE?

EVER WONDERED WHICH OTHER ANIMALS PONIES LIKE OR DISLIKE AND WHY? WONDER NO MORE!

PONY FRIENDS

SHEEP

Quite often horses and ponies are turned out with sheep in very large fields or where grazing needs to be controlled, and the two species appear to get along famously! Sheep tend to move out the way of ponies as ponies are (usually) bigger, and ponies are not intimidated by sheep.

Grazing happily!

WATCHPOINT!

Be aware that fencing that is suitable for ponies might not be for sheep – they could escape through it! And as sheep fencing often contains barbed or meshed wire it is unsuitable for ponies. Electric fencing is a good option for mixed grazing.

GOATS

Many horses and ponies have been known to make firm friendships with goats. They are also sometimes used as companions for stallions. Where another horse would rile a fiery stallion, a goat provides a non-threatening field or stable mate. The cost of keeping a goat is quite low, plus they're super cute, making them great companions!

Ponies ♥ goats

CATS

Although cats are not often a 24-hour-a-day companion for ponies (although some cats have been known to take a shine to a particular pony and spend all day in their stable), cats often roam yards and barns. Ponies get used to cats and accept their presence, and usually neither species bothers the other!

Yard sharers

"You're just like me – yay!"

OTHER PONIES

Ponies are herd animals and love nothing more than the company of, you guessed it, other ponies! As well as allowing them to socialise, ponies' natural survival instincts mean that they feel safe in a herd. Plus, who can blame them for wanting a friend of their own kind that shares the same thoughts and behaviours?

FOE

Scary but beautiful!

Pheasants are the untimate hacking nightmare! They have a tendency to leap out of hedgerows, squawking and scaring the living daylights out of unsuspecting ponies on a ride. Many ponies get used to them, but they can still get a good fright if they're caught off-guard!

DONKEYS

You might assume that all equines behave the same and all get along with each other. However, some horses and ponies are known to be absolutely terrified of donkeys! Not many ponies like it when they bray, but some seem to just have an irrational fear. Horses and donkeys also often don't live well together as they display different behavioural tendencies and routines.

What big ears you have...

FLIES

Flies are the bane of most ponies lives throughout the summer months, with their relentless bothering and biting. Some ponies are bothered more than others (particularly those with sweet itch) and can even become stressed or depressed by a constant assult from fies. It is always a good idea to invest in some fly protection for your pony to help keep him comfortable during summer.

Buzz off!

Us, scary? Never!

PIGS

Pigs smell. And the scent is very distinctive to ponies. They can also smell them from quite a way away. So if you ever hack past a place where pigs live, your pony could start becoming a bit nervous before you can even see the pigs. The noises pigs make don't help either, and the combination means that lots of ponies are scared of pigs.

IN QUESTION...

DOGS

"FYI that's *my* hay..."

Some horses get on fine with dogs and even make friends with them, while some others dislike them. Ponies that dislike dogs might have had a bad experience with an aggressive dog, or may just not be used to them. Ponies can also be aggressive to dogs, and may chase them out of their field!

COWS

Beware the noise!

Ponies often don't like cows as the noise they make is scary to many ponies, and smaller ponies especially might feel threatened by their size. Lots of ponies will pass cows out hacking, but would not be happy to live with or next to them. However, some people say that horses and cows can live together quite happily, like they do with sheep.

ROYAL EVENTER ZARA PHILLIPS ON FEELING NERVOUS:

"I think everyone gets nervous. It's all part of getting yourself prepared for what you're about to do. You've got to just do your best on the day, despite your nerves!"

FOUR STAR EVENTER FLORA HARRIS ON BUILDING A PARTNERSHIP :

"Spend lots of time with your pony, both in and out of the saddle. I give my horses lots of time and allow them to learn from their mistakes, but repeat exercises until I am sure they are happy and confident in their work."

RACING JOCKEY SAM TWISTON-DAVIES ON BEING IN A RIDING RUT:

"Always ask for advice if you are stuck!"

EVENING LEGEND LUCINDA FREDERICKS ON STARTING OUT :

"You need determination and patience, and to be as thorough as possible in your training."

TOP EVENTER PIGGY FRENCH ON JUMPING SCARY FENCES:

"You can't let yourself have negative thoughts. Face your fears!"

TOP TOP

TAKE ADVIC
THE BEST IN

CHIEF RIDER AT THE SPANISH RIDING SCHOOL OF VIENNA, ANDREAS HAUSBERGER, ON ACHEIVING GOALS:

"You must love the horse. There are sure to be ups and downs so you must be tough on yourself. Get used to blood, sweat and tears!"

AWESOME EVENTER FRANCIS WHITTINGTON ON GOING FOR IT!:

"Never be afraid to give something a go! If you get it wrong, it just highlights an area for further education to help your career progress."

TOP SHOWJUMPER LAURA RENWICK ON HAVING PATIENCE:

"Patience is a virtue! When I was younger I wanted everything to happen straight away but now I have realised that you only get out what you put in, and it's usually worth waiting for!"

LEGENDARY SHOWJUMPER TIM STOCKDALE ON SETTING GOALS:

"Set achievable goals so you can mark off the steps to your main goal. That way you'll always succeed."

TEAM GB DRESSAGE RIDER LAURA TOMLINSON ON FIRST PONIES:

"My first pony was a lead rein show pony, but I didn't want to do showing, I just wanted to go fast so we tended to part ways quite often! He taught me to sit tight, and that falling off doesn't matter!"

RIDER TIPS!

TOP SHOWJUMPER WILLIAM FUNNELL ON TAKING ADVICE:

"The best piece of advice I have been given is to keep one leg on either side of the horse! John Whitaker told me that!"

DRESSAGE LEGEND CARL HESTER ON TAKING CRITICISM:

"Accept criticism and use it to become a better rider. Also, try and film yourself riding so you can analyse your riding later on."

FROM SOME OF THE BUSINESS!

BADMINTON-WINNING EVENTER OLIVER TOWNEND ON FALLING OFF:

"If you fall off, get back on straight away if you can so that you and your pony don't lose confidence in each other."

Charlie, Charlene and Sofia are all enjoying the snow...

LOVING THIS SNOW! LOOK AT ALL THE WILDLIFE TRACKS.

OH WOW! I WONDER WHAT ANIMAL MADE THOSE.

I'M GOING TO GET SOME HOT CHOCOLATE. ARE YOU COMING CHARLIE?

NO, BRING ME BACK SOME. I WANT TO FIND THIS ANIMAL.

BRRRR. WAIT FOR ME, SOFIA, I'LL COME WITH YOU.

OH WOW! I WONDER WHAT ANIMAL THIS CAN BE? I'LL FOLLOW THIS ONE.

UH OH! THE FIRST TRACKS HAVE BEEN JOINED BY A SECOND SET. THERE ARE TWO OF THEM!

I HOPE THEY AREN'T VERY BIG ANIMALS...

THERE'S ANOTHER SET! THERE ARE THREE OF THEM!

HEY, CHARLIE, WHATEVER ARE YOU DOING?

WE'VE WATCHED YOU GO AROUND THAT COPSE THREE TIMES. AREN'T YOU GIDDY?

ER... UM.. NO. I THINK I'LL HAVE SOME OF THAT HOT CHOCOLATE NOW!

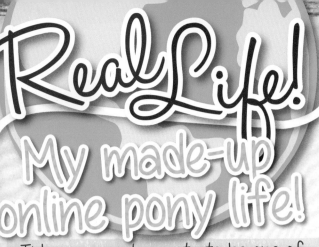

Real Life!

My made-up online pony life!

Tisha was so desperate to be one of the in-crowd, she went too far online...

I've always wanted a pony. My parents have always refused to get me one. I had a friend at school who rode, and she suggested I go riding with her. I liked the lessons but the thing was, unless you had your own pony there, the other girls who *did* have their own ponies didn't even know you existed, and I felt like a second-rate citizen. I so wanted to be part of the in-crowd but after I'd tried for the third time to talk to them, and been looked at like I was dirt, I stopped going for lessons. I just couldn't bear not to be included in the inner circle.

I BECOME A PONY OWNER

And then I discovered a local horsey website with its own online forum. The site was designed for riders in the local area, and all the people on it either had their own horses and ponies, or they rode. I registered, under a made-up name, and started replying to other people's queries, and soon it became obvious to me that in cyberspace, no-one would know whether I had a pony or not. So I invented one. To the rest of the forum members, I became a pony-owner.

I registered online, under a made-up name

BLACK WARRIOR

My first horse was Black Warrior. Warrior was, I told my online friends, a part-Arab stallion which I'd rescued from a man who beat him. I had always dreamed of owning a black horse, and Black Warrior was my dream. My online forum friends asked me questions about Warrior, and I answered them all, making up things left, right and centre. It was like having my own online fantasy life! Everything was going really well, and some of the other people on the forum started asking me questions about riding and behaviour like I was an expert, which I loved, when things got a bit too heavy.

"Where do you ride?" someone asked me.

"If Warrior is such a great jumper," another asked, "what shows will you be going to this season? We can all meet up!"

I decided that Warrior had to go. But why would I sell him? I made up a brilliant story about Warrior being highly sought-after by a breeder, who promised to keep him in luxury for the rest of his days, and I said it wouldn't be fair to prevent him from breeding wonderful foals. I had to let go. I had to let Warrior fulfil his potential.

I decided that Warrior had to go. But why would I sell him?

DARK BEAUTY

So I was without a horse – but not for long. Dark Beauty was my next horse. A Quarter Horse mare who used to be a reining champion, but had been retired after an injury. Of couse, I nursed her back to health, and soon I was riding her (in my dreams) all over the place. But I couldn't go far or compete – I thought that would be a good get-out clause in case anyone asked me. Other people uploaded pictures of their horses and ponies for everyone to see, so I found images on the net, pretending they were Dark Beauty. It wasn't too hard – I'd made her a dark bay with no white markings, and there were plenty of images online of horses matching that description.

As things progressed I got a bit more daring and decided Dark Beauty could have a foal – with Black Warrior, of course. This gave me plenty to write about, and everyone else seemed genuinely interested in how my imaginary mare was getting through her pregnancy. It actually taught me a lot about horse care, as I needed to do quite a lot of research.

I GO TOO FAR

Then I recognised one of the girls on the forum, Kathy. She kept her pony at the riding school where I'd gone for lessons, and she'd been really stuck-up with me. She wrote about her pony, Starbuck, and mentioned that she was going on a sponsored ride at the weekend – some 20 miles or so. Believing myself a bit of an expert by this time, and before I had thought it through, I posted that I hoped Starbuck had lost a bit of weight since last year, as he would find 20 miles a strain.

I'M BUSTED

All hell broke loose. Kathy got really upset and said Starbuck was just naturally round. Other forum users asked me how I knew Starbuck, as I had always told them I was out of the area. A woman who owned a livery yard said the forum was only for positive comments. Someone posted that they thought I was a fraud – that Black Warrior and Dark Beauty were obviously made-up names, and that I probably just had a rocking horse in the attic. Then someone else said the pictures I posted of my horses were clearly not in this country, and what did I think I was playing at? I couldn't believe it. I thought I had really convinced my fellow forum users, but it seemed I had fooled no-one.

LOOKING AHEAD

I've stopped using that forum. I may go and have some riding lessons again, and make more of an effort with the other pupils there. I've been a bit stupid, really, thinking I could fool people. I didn't. The only person I fooled was myself.

posed by models

53

1 + 2

HI ERIN. WANT TO GO RIDING?

HEY HESTER. YES, BUT HADN'T WE BETTER WAIT FOR JAKI?

I SUPPOSE SO...

WHAT'S UP?

LATER...

HESTER AND ERIN HAVE GONE RIDING WITHOUT ME. ON TOP OF EVERYTHING ELSE...

COME ON COPPER, LOOKS LIKE IT'S JUST YOU AND ME.

LOOK OUT, HERE COMES JAKI.

AND SHE LOOKS RIGHT MISERABLE, AS USUAL!

HI JAKI, CHEER UP, IT MIGHT NEVER HAPPEN!

YEAH, COME ON, GIVE US A SMILE!

= PROBLEM!

JAKI, HESTER AND ERIN WERE BEST FRIENDS. UNTIL JAKI WASN'T HER USUAL SELF...

IT'S JUST THAT JAKI HAS BEEN SO MOODY LATELY, AND SHE'S STARTING TO BRING ME DOWN.

I KNOW WHAT YOU MEAN.

LET'S JUST TACK UP AND GO. SHE COULD BE AGES, YET.

OKAY. SHE HAS BEEN A BIT OF A MISERY LATELY.

EVEN RIDING ISN'T HELPING...

OH COPPER, NO-ONE UNDERSTANDS BUT YOU. I'M SO GLAD I'VE GOT YOU TO TALK TO.

YOU JUST DON'T UNDERSTAND!

WHAT'S GOT INTO JAKI?

I DON'T KNOW, BUT IT SEEMS WE JUST MADE IT WORSE!

OOPS!

LATER, OUT RIDING...

YOU DON'T THINK JAKI IS UPSET JUST BECAUSE OF US, DO YOU?

I HOPE NOT. I MEAN, WE WERE JUST TRYING TO JOLT HER OUT OF THE BLUES.

BUT WHAT IF THERE'S SOMETHING WRONG, AND SHE'S NOT JUST BEING A MISERY?

I SUPPOSE THERE'S ONLY ONE WAY TO FIND OUT!

TRY US!

COME ON, LET'S TALK WHEN WE GET BACK TO THE YARD.

LATER...

SO WHAT'S THE PROBLEM, JAKI?

WELL, IT'S JUST THAT I'M NOT DOING VERY WELL AT SCHOOL, ESPECIALLY MATHS.

MATHS? I LOVE MATHS!

SIX WEEKS LATER...

YOU MEAN IT?

OF COURSE!

HEY, YOU'LL NEVER GUESS! I GOT TOP MARKS IN MY MATHS TEST YESTERDAY, AND MUM SAYS I CAN CHOOSE A NEW RUG FOR COPPER!

WOW! WHAT A TURNAROUND!

OPPER HESTER JAKI RUSTY ERIN GRACE

THE END!!!

STARRING: JESS AS JAKI, HANNAH AS HESTER AND ELLIE AS ERIN. HARELY AS COPPER AND RUSTY AND GRACE AS THEMSELVES!

Make a rozzie holder!

Why not display your rosettes with this snazzy holder? It can be used for photographs of your fave pony, too!

You will need

Some stiff cardboard
Wooden clothes pegs
Two bulldog clips
Ribbon
Paint, paintbrush,
PVA glue

How to do it

1 Cut a piece of cardboard the length you want your rosette holder to be. Ours was 73cms by 8cms.

2 Paint the board – you will need to do this on both sides, otherwise your cardboard will curl! Cover the table, like we did, so you don't get paint everywhere!

3 Once the paint is dry, take the wooden pegs and put PVA glue on one side of the top part of each peg, and glue them to the board, in intervals. Wait for the glue to dry.

4 We printed some horse silhouettes we found on the web and cut around them to stick onto the holder. You might prefer to use pictures of your pony, or write his name across the board, instead. It's up to you!

5 Once everything is dry, clip two bulldog clips onto the top of the board and tie some ribbon to these so you can hang up your rozzie holder. Then hang up your rosettes!

This makes a great gift for a horsey friend and you might like to experiment with different shapes – how about a horse shape, a horseshoe or even a herd of horses, all joined up? See what you can come up with!

Handsome HUNTERS!

The hunter is bred to follow hounds. He should be brave, safe and sound, and capable of covering the hunt's terrain. Today, a hunter is a great riding horse - you don't have to go hunting to enjoy a hunter!

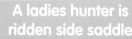
A beautiful hunter!

HE'S NOT A BREED!

Just like hacks, riding cobs and polo ponies, the hunter is a type of horse, rather than a breed. Many great hunters come from Ireland, but you find hunter type horses in all countries where hunting takes place.

WHAT makes a GOOD one?

A good hunter is capable of being ridden for most of the day over various country. Many good eventers make great hunters! A hunter needs to suit its rider – although there are still many hunter hirelings which are hired out to people without their own horses, to enjoy a day's hunting! The ability to stay sound and not fret or hot up is a necessary requirement, as well as carrying their riders at the gallop! Hunters should take everything in their stride!

SHOW HUNTERS

There are many different classes for show hunters, and a big show is a great place to see all the different ones. Hunters differ from hacks in that they are much heavier in build. They're an all-terrain horse, so need to be built more like a Land Rover than a Ferarri! Many good hunter types are Thoroughbred crosses – the hot blood of the TB helps them to fly across country – but a more stocky ancestor gives them the power and strength required.

A ladies hunter is ridden side saddle

SHOW US WHAT YOU CAN DO, THEN!

Show hunters need to be able to demonstrate that they can gallop, and are always asked to do so in the show ring. They are also ridden by the judge, so must be well mannered and well schooled.

There are classes for small hunters, lightweight, middleweight and heavyweight hunters and also for ladies hunters, ridden side saddle. The weight categories are judged on the weight the horses would be able to carry out hunting, as well as the height of the horses. Good bone – the circumference of the leg under the knee – denotes the weight horses can carry. The thicker, the better.

There are also classes for working hunters, where the horses are required to calmly jump a course of natural jumps, just as they would in the hunting field.

HUNTER TURNOUT

Show hunters are shown in plain tack – no coloured browbands – as if in the hunting field. Plain, wide nosebands are the norm, and you may see plaited reins (for grip) on the double bridles.

Riders wear hunting wear, and in evening classes and at the big and royal shows, gentlemen riders wear scarlet coats, mahogany top boots and carry a hunting whip.

A lovely grey show hunter

DYK?

Look out at shows for classes for Show Hunter Ponies. These are shown as hunters, and look just like hunters in miniature!

A working hunter at a show

pony puzzlers!

1. She's the queen of dressage! (8)

2. A PONY columnist and top showjumper (7)

3. A John who used to ride Milton, and is still top of his game (8)

4. Her first name is Georgina, but she's known by her porky nickname (6)

5. A top eventer – just don't call him Ollie! (7)

6. She events, she writes pony books, she wins Rolex Grand Slams... (7)

7. A young paralympian whose surname suggests she'd be better off cooking (5)

8. This top showjumper shares his first name with a famous London clock (5)

9. This female eventer's surname sounds like a male first name! (10)

10. This eventer shares a first name with a prince! (5)

11. This well-loved eventer has a regal surname (4)

12. An Olympic dressage rider from Sark (6)

13. She and Fernhill Sox were the 2007 Junior European Eventing Champions (7)

14. First name Scott, occupation top showjumper! (5)

15. A showjumper whose first name rhymes with Jim (9)

CAN YOU NAME THE HORSE OR PONY BREEDS FROM OUR CLUES?

1. Sounds like this pony *used* to live in a heather-covered place _____
2. Not a pony who lives in low places _____
3. Shares its name with a cow! _____
4. An American two-time pace and dog-like creature _____
5. Four of them make a whole _____
6. Not too steady on its feet? _____
7. Lives somewhere that doesn't sound old _____
8. A boxer from the East of England? _____
9. Go riding with supple joints _____
10. Shares its name with a cross country fence _____

spot the difference

THERE ARE 15 DIFFERENCES BETWEEN THESE TWO PICTURES OF CARRIAGE HORSES.

THERE ARE 10 DIFFERENCES BETWEEN THESE PICTURES OF PONIES PLAYING IN THE SNOW!

answers on page 98

CHOOSE YOUR PERFECT RIDING SCHOOL

Use this PONY guide to choosing the best riding school for you. If you can tick all the boxes, your perfect riding school should be found!

LOCATION, LOCATION, LOCATION

Sometimes, location governs which riding school you will go to. You may need to get there by bus, or by bike, or your parents don't want to drive miles and miles every week! Or perhaps there just isn't much choice! However, if there is more than one riding school in your area, and they all check out our list, use your gut feeling to choose the one which is right for you. Only you will know!

DO YOUR RESEARCH

Find out about any riding school you are considering. Does it have British Horse Society or Association of British Riding Schools approval for the current year? If so it will have passed an inspection to say the horses and ponies are fit and healthy, the instruction is sound and it has good facilities. But there are still riding schools out there without approval which offer good instruction. Trot along with your shortlist and take a look-see.

FIRST IMPRESSIONS

When you arrive at the yard does it seem quietly efficient? Is it tidy? Is it clean? Is there an office, fire extinquishers, notices, confident horses looking out over their doors? Do the staff greet you? Are they suitably dressed?

A yard with tools stewn around, instructors shouting and nobody taking any notice isn't good – so use your eyes and ears on that first impression.

INSTRUCTORS

They should be qualified, or in training for their teaching examinations. Do they seem friendly as well as efficient? Would you like them to teach you or do they seem a bit snooty, scary or disinterested?

PONIES

Every riding school should have a good selection of horses and ponies for all abilities. You want to progress in your riding, don't you? They should also be friendly and easy to handle. Take a turn around the yard and introduce yourself.

Is there a school (indoor or outdoor) in which to ride?

Tack rooms should be tidy

Is the yard neat and are the horses happy?

LESSONS

See if you can watch a lesson. Does it seem to be the sort of lesson you'd enjoy? (Or would you hate it?) Do the riders on it seem to be learning anything? (Or are they bored?) Are the riders at a similar standard? (Or are beginners mixed in with more experienced riders?) Do the ponies seem keen and willing? (Or are they naughty or lazy?) Is the arena in good condition? Where will you ride if it is raining, or windy, or snowing? A lesson in a waterlogged outdoor arena with grass growing in the middle may not be very appealing to you in the middle of winter!

FACILITIES

Check out the tack room – is it clean and organised? That goes for the feed room, too.

How far do you want to take your riding? Some riding schools have great cross country courses, or hold shows at the weekend.

Find out whether the riding school offers different lessons – side saddle or western for example. It all adds to the richness of your riding experience – although lessons may be a bit more expensive if there's plenty on offer!

GOOD LUCK WITH YOUR SEARCH!

PONY CLUB

Ask whether the riding school is a Pony Club Centre. This can really add to your riding experience – you can take the Pony Club tests and enjoy lectures and rallies.

OTHER POINTS TO CHECK

So we've looked at the cold facts but sometimes a riding school just feels right for you. It may not be very posh, or have a huge indoor arena, but the ponies seem cute and everyone is so friendly you can't wait to spend time there. As long as your chosen riding school is safe, and offers good instruction, it's all about personal preference. It's up to you!

How to find a riding school
Go to www.bhs.org.uk and www.abrs-info.org.uk to discover approved riding schools in your area.

Nothing but a dare...

PONY short story winner, by Natalie Somerville

COULD CASSIE PERSUADE HER SISTER TO SHARE HER PASSION – HORSES?

Hayley lay slumped on the sofa, watching TV. She held her breath as her sister Cassie walked in through the door. Cassie was just back from the stables and, in Hayley's opinion, stank of horses. Trying not to show how disgusted she was Hayley asked her, "How was your day?"

Cassie gave her a broad grin. "It was great! We did some jumping in the arena, and then went for a big hack. After that we gave the ponies a good groom and turned them out."

"Oh. Well I'm glad you had a good time."

"Yeah, it was so cool. You should come down to the yard sometime, Hayley."

Hayley shook her head vigorously in disagreement. "No thank you. I'm quite satisfied with the TV and my laptop. The only thing I'll ever ride, is a bike."

Cassie sighed with disappointmet and left her sister alone. She never came up to the stables. She never would. Hayley just didn't understand what it was like to gallop across fields on a horse, to feel the wind on your face and hear the low rumble of your horse's feet as they connected with the ground at every stride. That was the way is was forever going to be, and nothing could change that... or so she thought...

The beeping of the early alarm clock awoke Hayley. She opened her sleepy eyes and took her first peek at the new day. Cassie had already gone to the stables, so she figured she had a whole day ahead of peace and quiet. Hayley slowly rose from her comfortable position under the duvet and opened her curtains. She gazed whistfully out onto the bright morning sky. After five minutes of staring, she shook herself out of her daydream and, just to double check she was wide awake, had a shower.

After her shower, Hayley sat down at her desk to do some homework that she needed to catch up on. She scanned her homework diary and groaned. She had two essays, five pages of Maths and a History exercise.

"Well," Hayley said to herself, "better get started!" Hayley fished her history textbook out of her bag and read the cover aloud. "*Medieval History for High School Pupils.*" It didn't sound too bad, she decided. She turned to page 231, the desired pages, and read the first line. Hayley rolled her eyes. It read: *Amongst the many important weapons and supplies knights needed the most important, by far, was the horse...*

How could a horse be the most important tool to a knight, Hayley scoffed. But she was interested, and wanted to know the answer, so she read on.

... Horses were used in battle and hardly ever faltered. They fearlessly galloped into battle and took care of their riders. These magnificent beasts stayed with their masters until the very end...

> **HAYLEY JUST DIDN'T UNDERSTAND WHAT IT WAS LIKE TO GALLOP ACROSS FIELDS ON A HORSE**

Hayley was impressed. She never would have thought a horse would be as loyal as that. Okay, she had heard about how loyal dogs were, but a *horse*? Maybe she was wrong about them.

When Cassie came home, Hayley had just finished her humungous pile of homework and sat on her bed, reading. She could hear banging that was Cassie running up the stairs in her riding boots. When she came running into the bedroom, Hayley shrieked, "GET OUT OF HERE IN THOSE MUDDY BOOTS!"

Startled but unhindered, Cassie merely replied, "They aren't muddy – I cleaned them before I came in," and sat on the bed beside Hayley. Nevertheless, she yanked off her riding boots an threw them into a corner.

Hayley gave her an utterly disgusted look. Cassie grinned. "When you share a room with a horse rider, you have to get used to the mess."

Hayley knew Cassie had won the battle. She sighed in defeat and swapped her book for her laptop. She logged onto Google Plus and spotted some new posts. She turned to the first one, which had been posted by a user called *Horseridinglover*. The post had an image of a girl riding a horse across a field, and the text above the image read: *No-one has experienced true joy until they ride a horse. A horse is a girl's best friend, until the very end. Horse riding is one of the best ways ever to spend your time, and you never get bored! Between caring for a horse and riding it, there's loads to do. So do get up and ride!*

Hayley paused before looking at the other posts. Maybe horses weren't such a waste of time after all. She was knocked out of her thoughts by Cassie who, sitting beside her asked, "Anything good on the web?"

Hayley quickly exited the horse riding post and pretended to be commenting on something else. "Nope, nothing much – just the usual internet gossip, that's all." To her relief, Cassie believed her. She didn't want Cassie to know she was taking even the slightest interest in horses. She'd be harassing her non-stop to go down to the stables!

After that close call, Hayley decided to spend some time with her sister as she felt she hadn't been very nice to her lately. She closed down her laptop and asked her, "Cassie, what do you want to do?"

Cassie gave her a broad smile. "I dunno, what do you want to do?"

> **"HMMM, WHAT ABOUT PLAYING TRUTH OR DARE?"**

"Hmmm, what about..." said Hayley, "playing *truth or dare?*"

"Yeah! That sounds like fun!"

Hayley smiled. She knew Cassie loved this game. "Sorry, Cassie," she said suddenly.

Cassie looked up, surprised. "For what?"

"For being a mean sister and criticising your horse

riding... and, well, literally despising horses and everything to do with them!"

Cassie looked into her sister's apologetic eyes. "It's okay, Hayley, I know you don't like horses, and yes, it hurts when you criticise them, but I just accept that not everyone has the same passion for them as I do."

Hayley nodded in agreement. "Thanks for understanding, Cassie."

"Okay, let's get started."

"Truth or dare, Cassie?"

"Hmmm... dare!"

"I dare you to get a packet of marshmallows and put as many as you can into your mouth!" said Hayley.

"You're on!" laughed Cassie, running to get the marshmallows.

10 minutes later, the girls were in stitches as Cassie sat with her mouth bursting with marshmallows. After she finally managed to swallow them all, she declared it was her turn. "Truth or dare?" she asked Hayley.

"Dare."

"I dare you to... come to the stables with me tomorrow and ride."

Hayley sat in shock. Cassie's words hung in the air. She stared at Cassie. Cassie stared back. Finally, Hayley managed to force out a whisper.

"Is there any getting out of it?"

"Nope!" Cassie replied, firmly.

Before Hayley could protest, their mum stuck her head through the doorway. "Lights out, girls!"

Hayley checked her watch. It was 10.30pm already!

"Okay Mum," Cassie quickly replied, and hopped into bed, leaving a stunned Hayley sitting on her bed. After a minute, when the realisation of what had just happened sank in, she too climbed into her bed.

"Goodnight sis," said Cassie, into the darkness. "Big day tomorrow. Tomorrow, you are finally going to ride a horse! And I have the perfect horse in mind..."

Hayley gulped. It was nothing but a dare, she told herself. It wasn't like she was taking regular lessons or anything. She wasn't exactly scared about riding – she was petrified and amazed all in one! A small part of her was actually looking forward to the next day!

Bright and early the next morning, Cassie pulled Hayley out of bed.

"Good morning, sister. Ready for your big day?"

Hayley groaned loudly. There really *was* no getting out of this.

A little later, Hayley didn't recognise herself. She wore jodhpurs, a riding jacket and riding boots. She stared wide-eyed at her reflection in the mirror.

"You look like a professional rider!" Cassie reassured her.

"But I'm not a professional!"

"You might as well look the part," said Cassie. "Now come on, let's go!"

When the girls arrived at the yard, Hayley was surprised at how tidy it was. She had imagined a dusty, horse-poo-covered yard full of scruffy ponies. On the contrary, it was a tidy concrete yard with a sand arena and a stableblock full of well-groomed ponies.

Cassie waved a tall young woman over. Hayley felt uncomfortable as Cassie introduced her and explained the situation and why there were there. The lady laughed as Cassie explained how she had dared her sister to ride.

"My name is Kathy," she said. "I'm Cassie's riding instructor. I will be giving you a lesson today." Hayley and Kathy shook hands.

"Cassie, can you go and tack up Bolt and I'll show Hayley where the riding helmets are," Kathy instructed. Cassie nodded in agreement and ran off towards the stables.

"Bolt? You do know I'm totally inexperienced, right?" Hayley asked, worriedly.

"Don't worry, Bolt is completely bombproof," Kathy reassured her.

Hayley didn't know what that meant, but didn't want to seem even more like a dummy, so didn't ask. Kathy took Hayley over to a padlocked shed.

"What's in here that's so precious?" Hayley wondered out loud.

Kathy looked surprised. "The tack, of course!"

"Really? I didn't know saddles and bridles were so very expensive!"

Kathy laughed. "You really don't know anything about horses, do you?" she said.

"Nope, not a thing," Hayley admitted.

Hayley stood in the sand arena, waiting for her mount to arrive. She was terrified. Why hadn't she refused the dare? Soon, Cassie appeared, leading a chunky piebald that plodded along. All fears of being thrown were demolished. Now Hayley worried that she wouldn't be able to get 'Bolt' to move an inch!

She gulped as Kathy gave her a leg-up onto his back. Instead of bouncing lightly into the saddle, she landed like a sack of potatoes. But Bolt didn't flinch. Relieved that was over, but totally mortified, Hayley clumsily tried to get her reins in the right position. Kathy was patient. She gently showed her the right way and, after a few attempts, Hayley finally got it right. She kicked Bolt's sides and he lurched forward into a bouncy trot.

"That's it, up and down, up and down, well done!" Kathy praised.

Hayley was really enjoying herself. "This is so cool! I wish I had tried horse riding sooner!"

Cassie grinned. "I told you so!"

After the ride, Hayley thanked Kathy for instructing her, and Cassie for daring her to ride!

"Thanks so much, Cassie. I never realised how much fun riding actually is."

"It's okay, I'm surprised you actually came!"

"Well, if I had known I had an option, I probably wouldn't have, but I'm so glad I did. I'd like to come here regularly and maybe, after a few lessons, we can hack out together."

"Really?" said Cassie. "You mean it?"

Hayley nodded.

And Cassie could tell by the look in her eyes that she really did.

HAYLEY WORRIED THAT SHE WOULDN'T BE ABLE TO GET 'BOLT' TO MOVE AN INCH!

HORSESCOPES

Find out what 2016 holds for you and your special pony!

AQUARIUS
(January 21 – February 19)

2016 is the year when you will embrace new ideas about ponies and riding. It may be you need to listen to your inner voice – do you want to change your relationship with ponies? Don't be afraid to talk to others about your feelings, you have greater influence than you may think. Don't hesitate, however, to move on from those around you who are unwilling to grow with you, and may hold you back.

PISCES
(February 20 – March 20)

You can afford to be optimistic about the year ahead – don't be afraid to set goals to challenge you. Even if you do not achieve them all, you will learn by your efforts, which will not be wasted.

Although your friendships are strong, do not be afraid to follow your own path. Who says we all have to be the same? You may also feel drawn to a project at the stables, perhaps helping others, either human or equine.

ARIES
(March 21 – April 20)

The message this year is not to let past experiences hold you back. If you have worries about your riding, put these behind you and concentrate on a new period of learning and confidence. If sometimes you feel stressed, remember you have more control over situations than you may think.

Beware of over-committing yourself and your pony this year. Better to do few things well than lots of things badly, so you can look back on the year with a sense of achievement.

TAURUS
(April 21 – May 21)

Don't be surprised if 2016 is a year where you will be drawn to new experiences. Opportunities to learn new skills – maybe a different riding discipline like side saddle or western riding – may come your way, so don't waste them!

You should feel your confidence soar this year, but make sure this doesn't spill over into boasting, or feelings of superiority. There is always much to learn, and this year will be a great one for doing just that!

GEMINI
(May 22 – June 21)

Make 2016 the year you really decide where your dreams lie, and how you can achieve them. There will always be barriers to stop you, but you can find ways to smash through these (or go around them!), to stay focused on what you really want. But be honest with yourself. Where do you believe your talents lie? Give yourself and your pony the best possible chance to succeed by taking notice of your inner voice.

CANCER
(June 22 – July 22)

It could be that your responsibilities will increase in the coming year. Maybe you'll get a pony to care for, or someone will ask for your help. Partnerships are highlighted in your sign for 2016, and this could mean you get closer to a special pony in your life, or a new equine partner could be the pony of your dreams. Could the pony you already have be your dream pony? Maybe you just need to work a little more on your relationship!

LEO
(July 23 – August 23)

The year ahead promises to be successful, but it won't be achieved without effort on your part. This shouldn't be a problem for you but you may well feel restricted if this year starts as the last one ends. Don't let it! Seek new challenges and find joy in everything you do. You know the more effort you put in, the more you get out, and this is especially true of your riding and any competitions you enter. Hone your skills and success will be yours.

VIRGO
(August 24 – September 22)

You have a tendency to be serious about your riding – nothing wrong with that – but make 2016 the year you have fun! Remember that you can still learn while enjoying your riding – and your pony will lighten-up, too! Allow yourself to really get to know the special pony in your life, as a deeper understanding of his needs may well lead you to understand your own.

LIBRA
(September 23 – October 22)

You really feel the need to become more secure in your riding and pony handling ability, and this year should see this happen. Your confidence should soar, making things which seemed impossible last year, much easier to achieve. You should find that you are better able to face your fears, and this will lead to a horsey year to remember! Remember that to get support from others, you need to offer it yourself, so don't neglect your friends and you'll reap the rewards!

SCORPIO
(October 23 – November 21)

You often feel impatient with your riding, and can get quite annoyed by rules and regulations that may get in your way. Try not to worry if you feel rebellious. Make these feelings work for you by chanelling your energies into your riding to achieve greater results in competitions – or even when schooling at home. Don't forget that learning more about riding and ponies is an excellent way to make this energy work for you, and increase your self-confidence and self-worth.

SAGITTARIUS
(November 22 – December 21)

Who do you want to be? It's important for Sagittarians to ask themselves this question regularly. The problem is, who they want to be keeps changing! Don't worry, you can be all the people you want to be, but not all at once!

Take care this year that others give back to you as much as you give to them. Emotional energy can be draining, so ensure you keep some for yourself! Love for your special pony will never be wasted, so enjoy your relationship.

CAPRICORN
(December 22 – January 20)

Easy tiger! You can't wait for the challenges of 2016 to start – bring them on! It's great you're feeling confident and you should achieve many personal aims this year – all that work is paying off! Keep your feet on the ground, however, as being overproud of your achievments may be seen by others as boasting. Keep them onside with modesty. Throughout the year, see what clutter you can clear out (mentally and physically) to keep your aims clear.

FESS UPS!

YOUR CRINGE-INDUCING TALES FROM THE YARD...

TRIGGER'S A LAUGH

THIS IS HOW YOU DO IT...

It was my first day helping at my new riding school. I had been one of the top helpers at my old school, before we'd moved house, so was fairly confident. Having been asked to tack up Trigger, a lovely palomino, I leapt at the chance to demonstrate my ability. However Trigger kept putting his head up out of my reach.

One of the instructors, Brian, walked by and saw me struggling and took the bridle off me, showing me how to put it on. Trigger, course, was as *good as gold* with Brian, and Brian took great pains to tell me how it should be done. Just when I thought I couldn't feel any smaller, a group of girls walked past and heard Brian lecturing me. I felt about as low as I could get!

Pippa

EPIC EMBARRASSMENT!

NOT SO LUSCIOUS LUKE

My friends and I were sitting on the wall around the yard cleaning tack when Luke, my friend's brother, who is as fit as anything and known in our circle as *Luscious Luke*, joined us. Winking at me he squeezed between me and my friend Georgia, and I could feel myself going red. Suddenly, a spider ran up my leg, and I screamed, jumped in fright and felt myself falling backwards. I grabbed hold of Luke's arm but instead of saving me, I pulled him with me and we both fell. Everyone peered over the wall at Luke and me in an undignified heap, covered in dirty water from my tack cleaning sponge, and embarrassed as anything.

Luke never lived it down that I appeared to be stronger than him – which completely wrecked any chance I had with him!

Tammy

TOTAL EMBARRASSMENT!

OVER THE RAINBOW

I was grooming for my friend Shaz at a show, and had to go into the ring and help her as she untacked her pony Rainbow to run him up and down for the judge. Saddling up again, I gave her a leg up and, for the one-and-only time *ever*, we got the timing spot on and Shaz soared up in the air, flew over her pony's back and over the other side. Rainbow freaked and bolted around the ring, setting all the other ponies off.

When Shaz finally caught Rainbow, we were all asked to leave the ring in disgrace. Before that, Shaz had been lying in second place! Talk about embarrassment *squared!*

Gemma

EPIC EMBARRASSMENT!

NOT SO MAGIC MERLIN

SIT UP THERE!

At my riding school, I was asked to ride Merlin and give a beginners' ride a lead. Everything went well, and I was feeling rather smug because I'd had to demonstrate several movements which impressed the beginners no end.

At the end of the lesson we all lined up and prepared to dismount. Just then, Merlin decided to scratch his front leg with his teeth, and I almost flew over his neck onto the ground. Everyone laughed and my instructor told them not to copy me, and that I was demonstrating what NOT to do! Thanks Merlin!

Kailey

MEGA EMBARRASSMENT!

I FELT A RIGHT CHARLIE!

LIVE CAT JUMPS? NO WAY!

I had entered a clear round jumping competition at a nearby riding school and me and my friend Donna hacked over. It was a really informal affair – no-one had even dressed up in jackets and ties – and when I looked at the course I just knew my pony, Charlie, would easily get a clear round. Donna went clear and got a lovely, two-tier rosette in cream and blue, and I couldn't wait to put my rozzie on Charlie's bridle.

We entered the outdoor school and as the gate closed behind us, Charlie stopped dead, planting his front feet and refusing to move. Then I saw the stable's cat hiding under the first jump. Even when someone shoo-ed it out of the arena Charlie stood rooted to the spot. The cat had totally freaked him out!

After five minutes of legging on and getting cross with Charlie we were asked to leave as it was someone else's turn. I felt so stupid – there were tiny tots jumping clear and getting rosettes and I couldn't even get my pony to move! So embarrasing!

Maggie

TOTAL EMBARRASSMENT!

WHAT ARE YOU DOING IN THERE?

ONLY TRYING TO HELP...

I was walking through the livery barn when I noticed one of the liveries, Walter, was in his stable tacked up – but he'd wriggled out of his headcollar and had his bridle half hanging off his head. His owner was nowhere to be seen so I slipped into the stable and got Walter straight. I was about to tie him up again when his owner returned and demanded to know what I was doing in her horse's stable!

I protested my innocence, but she wouldn't listen and told me she'd report me to the stable staff if I continued to argue with her so I just sloped off. She told all the other livery owners to watch out for me – it was ages before I lived that down.

Celeste

EPIC EMBARRASSMENT!

THE DISAPPEARING HORSE

the first day in my new Saturday job, I was asked bring one of the horses in from the field. It was rk by this time, and I didn't realise that each stable d two doors, one at the front and another at the ck, so the horses could go out into the barn. I put e horse in the stable and shut the door, but when I ent to feed him, he wasn't there!

I spent 10 minutes looking around the yard before ealised about the door – it had been ajar and the rse had escaped into the barn. My boss found him unching hay, having trashed most of the bales. Was mbarrassed!

uren

EPIC EMBARRASSMENT!

WHAT A SLIP-UP!

I was showing one of the younger girls at my yard how to build up the muck heap on the trailer – getting the sides straight and patting down the top, when I noticed I had a number of other owners looking impressed. I kept going, feeling smug, and the heap looked pretty good. Taking hold of the wheelbarrow handles, I made my way down the plank to the ground again, only it was slippery and I skidded and fell over in a big pool of manurey water. I was soaked and everyone was sniggering!

My pupil quietly asked me whether I'd done it on purpose, just to get a laugh – which did *not* amuse me!

Caroline

TOTAL EMBARRASSMENT!

CAUGHT OUT BY TAMMY

I'd begged my friend Sam for ages to let me ride her pony and eventually, when she had to go out with her family for the day, she agreed. Tammy is only tiny – about 12hh – so I was fairly confident I wouldn't get into trouble, and I went riding with my other friend Vicki, on her pony Prince.

As soon as we got to the place Sam usually cantered, Tammy took off with me, ignoring all my aids to slow down, and leaving Prince standing. She refused to stop until we reached the far end of the field. When Vicki caught up with us, she was laughing so much, she almost fell off. She told everyone at the yard how little Tammy had totally taken charge. I was mortified!

Juliette

EPIC EMBARRASSMENT!

WHERE DO YOU THINK YOU'RE GOING?

Miniature horses

Miniature horses are essentially tiny versions of big horses – they aren't ponies! A miniature horse that is well bred should look like a scaled down version of a riding horse, and they often resemble the build of a light hunter or hack type. The maximum height for a miniature horse is 34 inches at five years old. That's about the same height as a large dog!

Teeny Falabella foals!

Miniature Shetlands

Minature Shetland ponies are smaller, finer versions of the traditional Shetland ponies – so they're not horses! They are more stocky than miniature horses but the maximum height for a miniature Shetland is the same – 34 inches. Standard Shetlands measure up to 42 inches.

Shetlands can be great fun to ride

An adorable miniature foal!

DYK?

Miniatures and Shetlands are typically measured in inches, not hands.

DYK?

Lots of minis live well into their 30s, while some even make it to their 40s or even 50s!

The Shetland Pony Grand National is always a big hit!

Little legs sure can move!

Mighty

MINIATURE HORSES AND PONIES ARE SUPER CUTE! THERE'S NO DENYING IT. BUT THEY'RE NOT JUST CUTE AND CUDDLY, MINIS ARE AMAZING IN MANY WAYS. CHECK OUT OUR FUN FACTS AND TOTALLY ADORABLE PICS!

Falabellas

Falabellas are a type of miniature horse which originated in Argentina. They typically stand between 30 and 34 inches high – so some are really tiny!

Minis make great companions...

No matter the size difference!

The small size of miniature horses and ponies means they are great for young, disabled and elderly handlers, as they are more managable then a big horse! Their good temperaments and cuddly looks make them great pets, but they can also be taught to jump, learn tricks, ridden by very small jockeys and even be driven! They make great therapy ponies, visiting schools, nursing homes and hospices. Twiggy, the adorable miniature horse, has a full time job as a therapy pony!

Minis are super friendly!

Miniature horse Twiggy, miniature donkey Mr Kipling and Shetland Super Noodles in height order!

DYK?

Some miniature horses can be trained as guide animals to help people who are blind. They are largely successful because they are smart, friendly and live longer than dogs.

DYK?

The British Miniature Horse Society was founded in 1992 to promote the welfare, breeding and showing of miniature horses.

Minis!

DYK?

Miniature horses can be any colour, and Shetlands and miniature Shetlands can be any colour apart from spotted.

Real Life!

My dad almost killed my ponies!

A simple mistake almost cost Vicky's ponies their lives!

When we moved to a cottage in the country, I finally got a pony! With a paddock at the back of our garden, rented from the farmer, we quickly installed Basher, my new Welsh pony, and his companion Twig, a mini skewbald. I was in heaven! Even more so because the village was heaving with other horsey people, including my new best friend, Emma.

Emma and I quickly fell into a dreamy routine of riding, caring for our ponies and talking horse. Black gelding Basher (real name Bish-Bosh-Tosh of Gustimore) was a dream. He was cute and cuddly, but no slouch. We had some fabulous rides around the countryside.

Of course, it wasn't all blissful. Especially the day Basher and Twig escaped from their field and ran riot around Dad's precious garden. There were hoofprints all over the lawn, Dad's pride and joy, and he was not so much angry as heartbroken, which was worse.

"I'm really sorry," I said, almost as upset as he was. "I'll do whatever it takes to make the lawn great again."

"Get a padlock for that gate, Vicky," my mum suggested, with a edge in her voice.

"It should recover for spring," my dad gulped. "It's only grass." But of course, I realised it was more than that to him. Dad lived to garden, and I knew it wouldn't be long before his lawn and flowers would be the talk of the village. Dad was so totally understanding about my passion that I was determined to be understanding of his. It was a matter of mutual respect.

SPRING AT LAST

That first winter was long and hard, and spring was a long time coming, but then, one day in late April, the sun decided to come out and I turned Basher out without his rug. He rolled and rolled, leaving a huge patch of shed coat in his paddock. I could hear my dad mowing the lawn – the hoofprints had long faded – and I gave Basher and Twig some carrots before meeting Emma on the bus to shop at the big tack shop in town. We had a great time and stayed late, enjoying a pizza before catching a later bus back.

SOMETHING'S WRONG

As soon as I walked into the field, I knew something was wrong. Basher was standing with his head down and instead of neighing a welcome to me and cantering over for his tea, he ignored me. Twig was lying under a tree, rolling first over one way, then back again.

With a feeling of dread I ran over. Basher was sweating and as I stroked his face he turned and looked behind him, cow-kicking at his stomach.

Colic! I felt hot and cold all over as I ran and got Basher's headcollar, leading him to his stable. Luckily, his bed was already laid, and I left him there, looking miserable, while I coaxed poor little Twig to his feet and put him, in turn, in his stable next to Basher. Then I pulled out my mobile and called the vet.

QUESTIONS, QUESTIONS

It seemed like hours before she arrived, but when she did she got to work immediately, giving them both a relaxant and listening to their gut movements – or lack of them. Twig kept trying to roll, and the vet instructed me to get him to his feet and stand quietly with him, to stop him hurting himself. Basher looked so miserable, I couldn't help crying.

Mum and Dad were there, and the vet started asking me questions: What did my ponies eat? Were there any poisonous plants in the field? Had I changed their diet at all? Could anyone walk past or through the field and feed them anything?

LETHAL GRASS

No, no, no, I replied. Nothing had changed. I checked the field regularly. No-one walked past the field. Then my dad turned pale.

"I threw the grass cuttings over the fence," he said. "I saw them eating them, a couple of hours later."

We ran out to see – the clippings had been in a pile by the fence, and in just a few hours they had heated up inside, causing the colic.

"I'm so sorry, love," Dad said, tears in his eyes. I didn't know what to say. He hadn't known grass clippings could be lethal to ponies.

NO MORE CUTTINGS!

Basher and Twig recovered – thank goodness. I can't describe how I felt when I'd seen them suffering. Dad now knows not to throw grass clippings over the fence for the ponies. They go in the compost now. My dad almost killed my ponies – and he'd thought he was doing them a favour!

Basher ignored me...

PLAIT ATTACK!

TRAD PLAITS

Only short manes can be plaited in the traditional way. Each plait starts as a bunch, and is plaited tightly, rolled or folded under a couple of times, then fastened either with a plait band, or sewn in with matching thread. You can also use sticky tape over plaits – contrasting colours look snazzy – or how about blinging it up with special diamanté plait bands?

THERE ARE MANY AND VARIED WAYS TO PLAIT A HORSE OR PONY'S MANE AND TAIL – HERE ARE JUST SOME OF THEM!

And this is how you sew them!

Traditional plaits – mmm, nice!

MANE TOO LONG?

If your pony has a long mane, you can still plait it – but don't try the traditional method because the plaits will be too big and lumpy!

DYK?

There should be an even number of plaits along the neck – plus the forelock!

DYK?

The higher the number of plaits, the longer the pony's neck will look, so if your pony has a short neck, put in more plaits – and plait right down to the end of the withers to make it appear longer!

Roses on a Spanish horse!

Shire horse with flights (flags)

Detail showing the mane plaited with raffia

A trellis tail

Unusual – but why not?

RUNNING PLAIT

Also called a Spanish plait. Start behind the ears and plait three bunches together – then work along the neck, adding more mane as you go along. Pull the mane tightly to keep it in place.

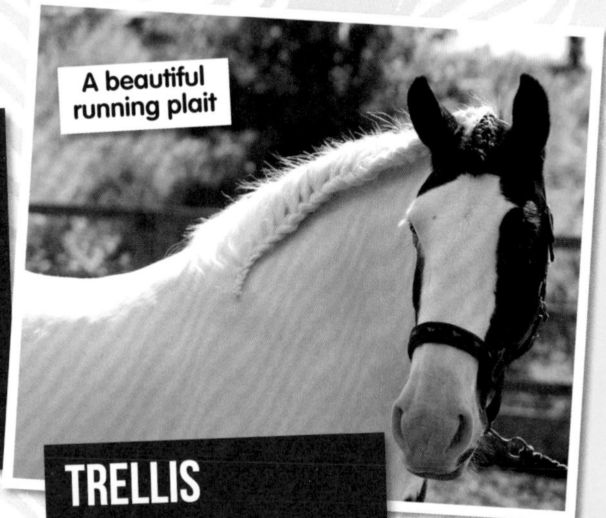

A beautiful running plait

TRELLIS

This is a fun way to dress a long mane – just bunch the mane evenly, then divide each bunch into two and fasten it with its neighbour until you run out of mane.

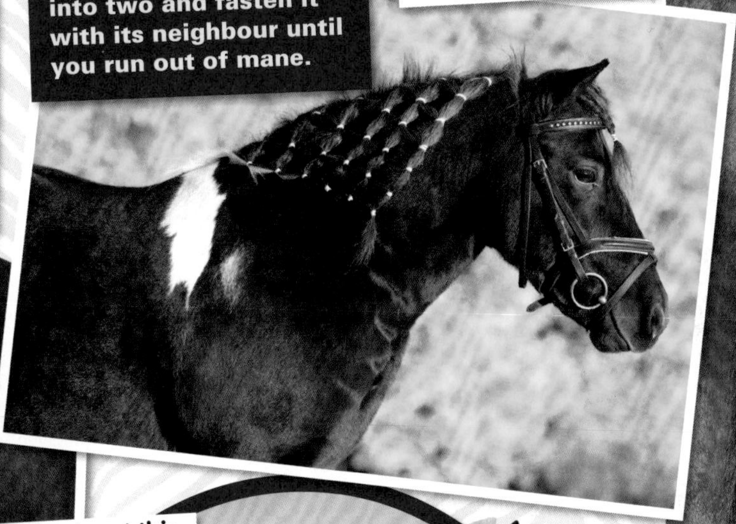

Cute trellis mane!

DYK?

If you see a red ribbon fastened to a pony's tail, it means Look out, I kick! A green ribbon means the pony is young, and therefore likely to be unpredictable. White means the horse or pony is for sale. Show jumping stallions wear red, white and blue tail ribbons at shows.

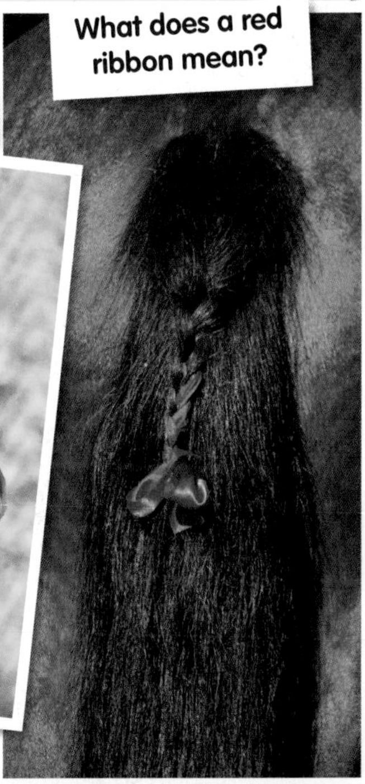

What does a red ribbon mean?

TAIL PLAIT

Plaiting a tail makes it look neat – but you can't plait a pulled tail! You need to bring the long hairs from either side of the dock in to a plait in the middle, and it takes a lot of practice!

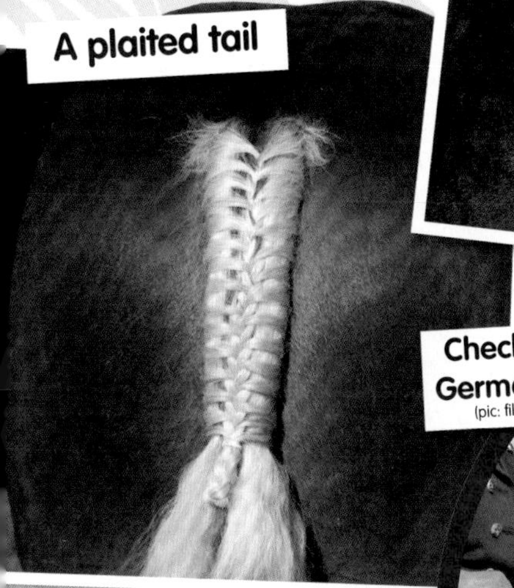

A plaited tail

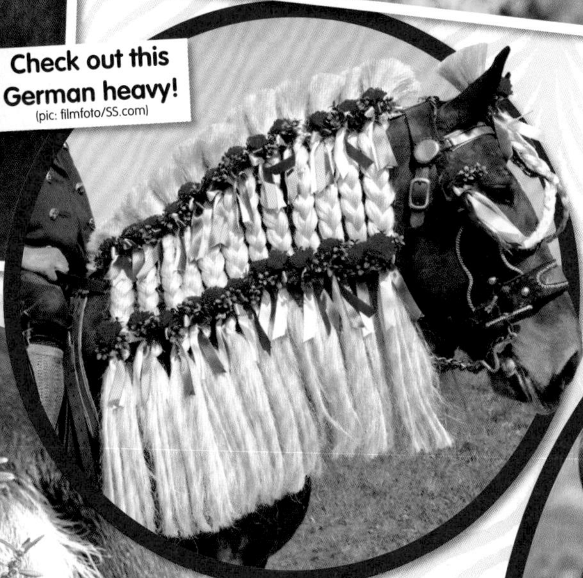

Check out this German heavy!
(pic: filmfoto/SS.com)

Why not have some fun inventing different ways to plait and dress your pony's mane and tail?

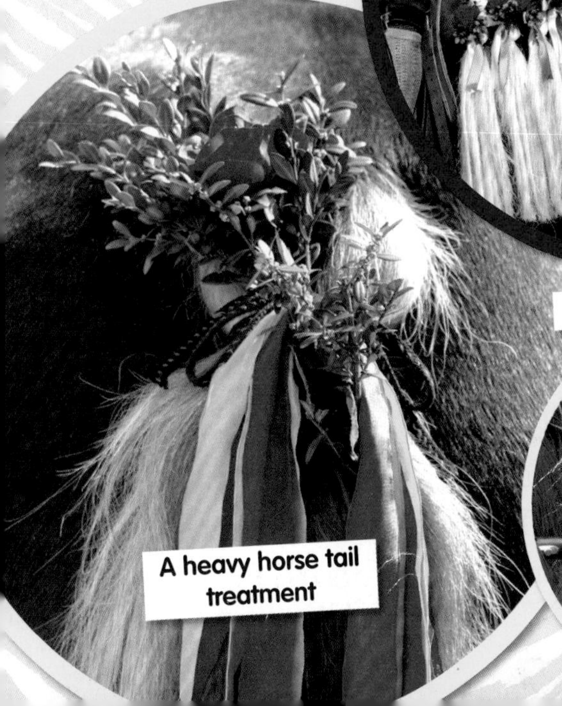

A heavy horse tail treatment

A woollen braid

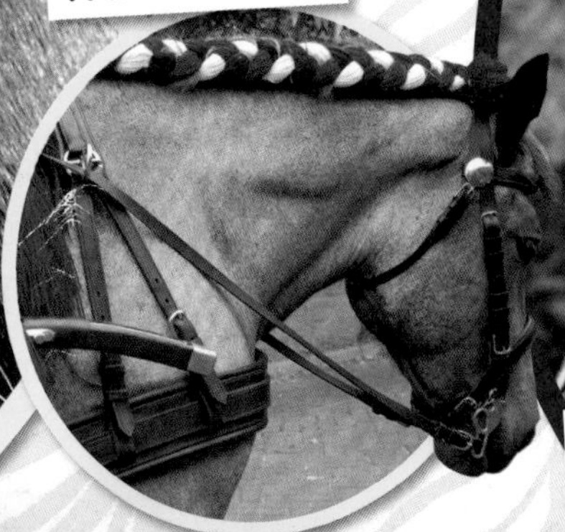

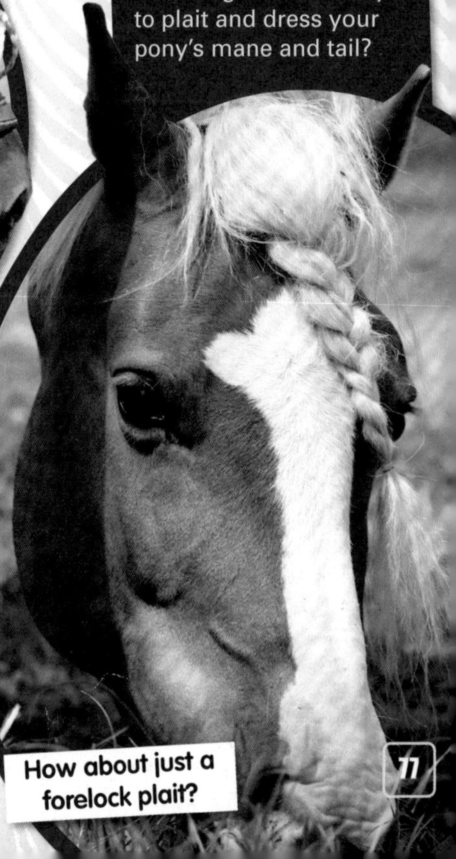

How about just a forelock plait?

HOW TO BE IN BALANCE WITH YOUR PONY

To be in balance with your pony you must first have a good position. A good position allows a rider to apply the correct aids, ride with maximum efficiency and therefore stay in balance with their pony through all the paces. Check that your hips are square in the saddle and you're sitting straight. Any unlevelness, however slight, will unbalance your pony. Suppleness through your hips and flexibility of your spine and shoulders allow you to remain in balance. Tensing your body will make it more difficult for you to go with the movement and will therefore affect your balance. Think relaxed and loose!

WHY IS IT SO IMPORTANT?

Horses and ponies are very sensitive. They can feel every movement you make with your body through their body. Any time you are out of balance, you pony knows it. Many ponies in riding schools have learned to become tolerant to this and carry beginner riders who are learning how to balance. Other ponies will not be so tolerant of out-of-balance riders, so it is an important element of your riding to get right!

POSITION

Every time you ride, make sure your position is as accurate as it can be. Not only does a correct position look far better, it means you will ride more effectively and your pony will be more responsive.

A common problem is for riders to start off in a correct position, but slowly let it slip or bad habits creep in to affect it. To make sure your position is consistant, every few minutes go through a position checklist in your head:

- **Am I sitting up tall?**
- Am I straight?
- **Are my legs too far forward or back?**
- Is my weight in my heels?
- **Are my elbows relaxed and bent?**
- Are my hands just above my pony's withers?
- **Is my rein pressure even?**

All these elements working together will help you to maintain your balance.

WATCHPOINT!

It is very important for riders to develop an *independant seat*. This is when a rider does not rely on their reins for balance.

Check your position to help maintain your balance

BALAN

Perfect balance takes practice. Check out why balance is so important and our top tips on how to achieve it!

A secure jumping position takes practice

JUMPING POSITION / FORWARD SEAT

To keep in balance with your pony when jumping, you will need to adopt a forward seat (jumping position). A correct forward seat takes a lot of practice, and this practice is tough on a rider's legs! You will need to shorten your stirrups two to three holes. This closes the angles at your knees and ankles, which will make you more secure and helps you keep your balance. Fold forward from your hips and keep your back flat, and make sure you keep your legs secure and in the correct position.

Practising your forward seat will help your balance. Ride in walk, trot and canter so you learn to hold your balance with the movement of each pace. The most important factor in a forward seat is that the rider's weight is balanced over the pony's centre of gravity.

BALANCE EXERCISES

To perfect the position of your hands, ride holding a whip on top of your hands with your thumbs on top of the whip. This will keep your hands steady and in the right place. It will also keep them even, which will help you maintain a steady contact and prevent you from leaning on your hands – you will have to use your seat to maintain your balance.

Balanced hands = even contact

Riding without stirrups is a great way to improve your balance and the effectiveness of your seat. It helps you feel the movement of the horse without having your stirrups to rely on for balance. Your position will have to be correct to keep you secure and balanced in the saddle.

To really test your balance, see if you can get an instructor to give you a lunge lesson with no reins, then no stirrups, then neither!

Remember to stay relaxed – If you're tense you will have a far more bouncy ride!

WATCHPOINT!

Only try exercises that require you to ride without stirrups or reins on an experienced, quiet pony in an enclosed arena with a qualified adult present.

The ultimate balance test!

The agile Polo Pony!

He's not a pony – but this horse is always called one!
Meet the polo pony!

It's not for wimps!

The game of polo is one of the world's fastest ball games, and is played on the biggest sports pitch! The sport is over 2,500 years old, and was played in ancient Persia and China, before migrating to India. Polo comes from the Tibetan word for ball, *pulu*. British soldiers serving in India took up the game and developed the specialist polo pony we know today.

They've gotta be brave!

Polo is played by a team of four on polo ponies, and the object of the game is to get the most goals – the ball is hit by the riders from their horses by a mallet (stick) held in the rider's right hand. Left-handed players must use their right!

Played at the gallop, the game requires fast, tough, brave and agile mounts, able to gallop and turn on a sixpence! As it is so fast and furious, each match is divided into chukkas, each of which last for only seven-and-a-half minutes, and ponies are changed after each chukka.

Running a polo team is a rich person's sport – you have to have a lot of ponies!

It's a team sport

Polo ponies play a team game, and are often exercised in batches – one groom may ride one and lead three or four others – so they have to get on!

Ponies or horses?

Originally, polo ponies were small – only about 12.2hh – which explains their name. However, modern polo ponies stand between 15-15.3hh, so are really horses, but they are always referred to as ponies.

Most polo ponies today are Throughbred crosses, and the very best – Thoroughbred x Criollos – come from Argentina, the polo pony capital of the world. Some of the very best polo players are also Argentinian! Polo ponies are not a breed but a type.

Dress sense

Polo ponies are always hogged (to avoid their manes getting in the way of the reins), and their tails are plaited and tied up so they can't get tangled up in the polo sticks. They wear special bandages on their lower legs to prevent injuries from the ball.

Argentinian polo ponies are famed for their speed and courage, as well as possessing ball-sense – a bit like quarter horses who posses cow-sense.

DYK?

Polo is played at Pony Club! You don't need a top polo pony, you can enjoy polo on any pony. Why not ask whether you can give polo a go?

All-weather playing

Polo is played not only on grass, but also on snow! Popular tournaments are played at St Moritz, in Switzerland, and form part of the society season. The polo ball is usually red so the players can see it in the snow.

DYK?

Look out for polo pony classes at selected shows. There aren't many, but they're worth seeking out.

FREEDOM

By Madelaine Randall, PONY short story winner!

Can the horse of Tessa's dreams help her escape from the life she hates?

This time it felt real. I thought I could feel his silken mane brush against my fingertips. I thought I could hear his breathing. I thought I could smell his heavenly scent. He smelt like freedom.

I awake, my hands outstretched, searching for him. My dream stallion. He is always in my dreams. I have named him Inferno. He is a chestnut colour, Arab build, with a white-hot flowing mane. I daydream about him, and soon find myself melting in his mocha-brown eyes.

My stallion is free like the wind. I am trapped like a bird in a cage too small.

I have lived with my uncle since my parents died in a tragic car crash. He makes me work for my keep. I have to do everything he says. I press my face to the window, staring outside, watching my uncle's prize racehorse, Silver Whirlwind, being lunged. I'm not sure why I'm watching. I loathe my uncle. He is one of those men that you want to report to the RSPCA. His whole racing life is a scam, except he's filthy rich for it.

CRACK! I hear the sound of the whip brought down on Silver's flank. He rears up, eyes wild. CRACK! again. Now I can't watch any more.

I sigh and lean back into my pillow. It is Silver's big day tomorrow, the Derby. I should get up to go to work, but I yawn and stretch, smiling to myself while I sink down into my bed and into my dreams again.

This dream is the most vivid I have ever had. I am galloping fast on Inferno, I can feel the wind and his mane falling back into my face as we gallop on. It feels 100 per-cent real. But then Inferno rears and I tumble off his back. Inferno sinks his head to the ground, then canters off.

"Tessa?"

My eyes flutter open. "Oh, Uncle, it's you. What is it?"

Uncle scowls. "You're always asleep, girl. I swear you are like a lazy sloth, sleeping for ages!"

"Oh..."

"Well, come on!" Uncle's gnarled hand closed around my arm. "You've got to earn your keep," and he pulls me so hard I think my arm might pop from its socket.

As soon as Uncle flings open the kitchen door that opens into the yard, my ear drums nearly split as I hear the distressed cries of horses.

"Ugh, what's going on?" My eyes dart around. Nothing unusual... yet.

Uncle gives me a shove. "Run, go find out what the problem is. Hurry!"

So I take off, my feet pounding hard on the ground, heart racing. I am soon approaching the field where Uncle turns out all his Thoroughbreds, but my heart stops as soon as I see what the problem is...

"It's you..."

He stands there, my Inferno, his eyes fixed on me. Is this a dream? I pinch myself on the wrist. Pain shoots up my arm. No, it's not a dream. I take one step towards him. He gallops, full speed, to me. It feels like we are the only creatures in the world. Time seems to slow down. Inferno has nearly reached me. I close my eyes and inhale his scent. Mmmm, smells like freedom.

Inferno kneels as if beckoning me to leap up onto his back. I clamber on. I soon realise I'm shaking. Well, you can't blame me, I've never been on a horse before. I take a breath, relaxing, before Inferno leaps forward like Uncle's Thoroughbreds on the track.

"Whoa!" I'm wobbling around like a useless blob of jelly, but soon my legs and arms lock themselves into a stable position. "Whew!" I breathe out. "It's okay," I reassure myself.

"TESSA LILA WALLIS!" My heart skips a beat. Uncle is at the gate, his ghastly face purple with rage. "What do you think you are doing?"

I don't have time to reply as I see what Inferno is about to do. The gate looms in front of us, and Inferno is galloping straight for it! I close my eyes and listen to the thundering of his hooves. It's all right, I'll be fine... I try to comfort myself. Not working! A voice is my head is yelling, *Woo hoo, something dangerous!* Another is shouting, *No, no, jump off or you'll die!*

The fence is about a stride away. Inferno flies over it – but in mid-air he kicks out, destroying the wooden planks that have imprisoned Uncle's racehorses for years. Scared and confused, Uncle's Thoroughbreds blindly flee, following Inferno.

"No! You're wrecking my business. Stop! NOW!" roars Uncle, but I am not listening.

Inferno gallops for what seems like hours, and in the end he and the Thoroughbreds collapse in a meadow, Uncle's shouts and screams still echoing in my head.

I slide off Inferno, my head spinning. How is this possible? I thought Inferno was only in my dreams, but here his is real. But then perhaps I don't need to know what is happening. I am here with Inferno, and free...

I brush stray strands of hair out of my eyes and lie back, staring at the azure blue sky. Today went by too quickly. The reality was beginnning to sink in. I'm alone. Nothing to eat. Nothing to drink. What am I going to do?

Then I feel Inferno tugging at my sleeve. I get up. At first I don't do anything, but then he tugs so hard I nearly fall over. Inferno bucks and then trots off. I don't want

> He stands there, my Inferno, his eyes fixed on me. Is this a dream?

> This dream is the most vivid I have ever had. I am galloping fast on Inferno, I can feel the wind and his mane falling back into my face.

him to leave, so I jog after him. A short distance away I see him standing under a tree. An apple tree! I rush and pick the delicious fruit and start to eat. I crunch into one, and its juice moistens my tongue. I give Inferno one to eat as well.

It is only later that I realise it's not the apple season. How had Inferno shown me a tree full of apples? I don't know, but I love Inferno more than anything. He is the best thing that has ever happened to me.

The sun is beginning to set, making the sky shine like liquid gold. I lie in the grass of the meadow. The horses are guzzling grass nearby. I must have taken a nap because when I awake it is nearly pitch black.

I huddle up close to Inferno. I use Silver's rug as a blanket, but still the cold of the night seeps through into my bones.

Morning soon rolls by, I am awake at dawn. My stomach tightens, not because of hunger, but because I don't feel Inferno's heat next to me. I leap up and look around. The other horses are grazing, but I can't see Inferno anywhere! My heart starts racing and my body starts shaking. How can he be gone?

Then I hear a low wicker. I spin around – and there he is, Inferno, head high, cantering to me. He comes to a halt in front of me, sinking down on his front knees. I embrace him, burying my face in his mane.

But then I'm aware of another noise. It's a car! My heart is racing quicker than the flow of a waterfall. My head is soon clouded with thoughts. They're going to take me away. No! What are they doing? Too late, the car is here.

It's a black Land Rover. The sun reflects on the smooth metal. Thoughts are rushing through my mind. Who is this? What do they want? The car door opens and then closes with a BANG!

Out steps a middle-aged lady. She has a sleek, black plait   tumbling down her back and   she's wearing a

blue polo and cream jodhpurs.

"Is this your stallion?" the lady asks.

I gulp and nod.

"I heard him outside my house this morning. He seemed to want to tell me something, so I decided to follow him."

She looks around the field, noticing the Thoroughbreds, and the crumpled horse rug on the ground. Then she looks at me.

"Where do you live?" she asks cautiously.

I don't know what to say. I don't want to say I live with my uncle because I don't want to go back there.

Then she sees something she recognises. "Isn't that Silver Whirlwind?" she asks.

"Yes," I say at last.

"And..." she's looking at me intently now, "... then you must be Tessa Wallis?"

My eyes widen in alarm. She'll take me back to my uncle! The lady must have seen my fear because then she says, "Don't worry, I was your mother's best friend."

"Who are you?" I ask.

"Olivia Rose," she says. "Your mother and I were very close. I tried to see you after your parents died, but your uncle refused to allow it."

Inferno neighs. We turn to look at him. He swishes his tail and returns our gaze.

"I do believe," says Olivia, "that your horse brought me to you. It must be for a reason. Would you like to live with me?"

I would! She was so nice, so much nicer than my uncle. But... "Can my horses come, too?" I ask.

"Of course," she says. "I have a farm. You can all stay with me."

So we spend the rest of the day taking the horses to Pinewood Farm, Olivia's home. It is lovely. The horses are happy galloping free without the whip of my uncle. I have a pretty bedroom overlooking the stables. From there I can watch Inferno.

> Then I hear a low wicker. I spin around – and there he is, Inferno, head high, cantering to me.

Posed by models

We are very happy. Then, one day, I look out of the window and can't see Inferno. I rush down to the stables. He isn't there, nor in the fields. With tears in my eyes I ask Olivia if she knows where he is. We both search high and low but he is nowhere to be found. I sit down on the stump of a tree. Big sobs came out of me and Olivia, oh so gently, puts her arm around my shoulders.

Inferno had come to me in my dreams when I needed comforting. He had rescued me from my cruel uncle, shown me apples when I was hungry and brought Olivia to me so I could live with her. He had freed me.

"Do you know," says Olivia, "Inferno may be gone for now, but I think he'll be back if you need him."

I look at Olivia through my tears. Suddenly, I feel Inferno is very close. He's not actually here, but he is in my heart. I know Olivia is right.

Découpage a tray!

A découpage tray is useful as well as pretty cool – and each one will be totally unique!

You will need

A tray – any old tray will do!
An old book
Old copies of PONY Mag and other pony books
PVA glue
Paint brush
Clear varnish

How to do it

Make sure your tray is clean and dry.

Tear strips from the book to create a base. Tearing is better than cutting as you get an edge which blends, rather than hard lines.

Thin the PVA glue with water, and glue the paper strips to the tray, overlapping them so the tray is completely covered. Use the glue on top of the paper, as well as below.

When the glue is dry, trim the edges of the tray.

Now tear pictures from your PONY Magazines. Don't worry if they are not tidy – it really doesn't matter!

Paste the torn images onto the tray, over the book pages, and as you did before, glue over the top, so all the edges are really tightly stuck.

The idea is to have a mish-mash of images, rather than neat rows. The more crowded it looks, the better!

DYK?

Découpage is from the French word *découpe*, meaning to cut out, and has been used for many years to decorate items!

Leave each layer to dry thoroughly. Keep adding layers until you are happy with the result.

Once dry, give the whole tray a couple of coats of clear varnish, leaving it to dry between coats. Two or three thin layers are better than one thick one.

Your finished tray can be used wherever you like. Why not make a truly individual horsey gift for a friend?

PONYMAG.COM

Keep up-to-date with all things horsey between issues of PONY Mag! It's the *only* horsey website you'll ever need!

WATCH
AMAZING VIDEOS ONLINE

WIN
WITH OUR FABULOUS ONLINE COMPETITIONS

PLAY
PONY GAMES – EXCLUSIVE TO PONYMAG.COM!

LEARN
FROM GREAT PONY MAG ADVICE

SEND
US YOUR PICTURES, LETTERS, FESS-UPS, REAL LIFE EXPERIENCES AND MORE!

JOIN
DUGGIE, SOLOMAN AND THE COLONEL AS THEY BLOG, BLOG, BLOG

BROWSE
THE PONY SHOP FULL OF CLOTHES, BOOKS, BAGS ETC – AND ALL THINGS HORSEY

SEE
INTO THE FUTURE WITH THE PONY HORSESCOPES

TEST
YOURSELF WITH THE AMAZING PONY QUIZZES

CATCH YOU AT
PONYMAG.COM

Real Life!
The pony of my dreams!

Vicki and Jaffa were made for each other – but would they ever be together?

I had always wanted to go on a riding holiday, so when my parents booked me a week at Hillside Riding Holidays, in Cornwall, you can imagine my excitement. I researched all the horses on their website and hoped beyond hope I would be allocated a cute-looking chestnut called Jaffa – although *any* horse or pony would be brilliant, of course.

CHEEKY JAFFA!

When I arrived at Hillside, I immediately palled up with a girl called Amanda, who was a year older than me. When we were allocated our ponies I couldn't believe my luck – I was given Jaffa! He was just brilliant – so cool! He was cheeky in the stable, but really affectionate. He loved having his ears pulled gently, and he would nose about my pockets for the treat he knew I always had for him.

I couldn't believe my luck – I was given Jaffa!

Amanda was teamed up with a skewbald called Clown, and we had the best week riding out on hacks, having brilliant instruction (Jaffa could jump like anything, and I learnt masses on him in just the few days I was there). One day, we even rode on the beach! Jaffa played in the surf and we had a brilliant gallop over the sands. Needless to say, when it came to say goodbye to my wonderful chestnut boy at the end of the week, I was in floods of tears. My mum, when she came to collect me, looked worried, I was in such a state.

Just to torture myself I would log onto the Hillside website to keep up-to-date with Jaffa

"Come on now, Vicki," she said, giving me a pat, "you knew you were going to have to leave Jaffa behind. He'll be okay – and when you go back to the riding school, you'll be reunited with Nutkin, your favourite pony. Have you forgotten him?"

"Of course not," I sobbed, "but Jaffa is so special – it's like he and I are soul mates. I know he'll miss me, too."

NOTHING IS THE SAME

Of course, it was no use. I had to leave Jaffa and for a few weeks, everything went back to normal. I went and rode at the riding school and looked after Nutkin as best I could, but things were just not the same. I remembered how much fun I had had with Jaffa, how he had raided my pockets, how he'd picked up grooming brushes and thrown them over his stable door, the cheeky way he nickered to me when I went out to catch him in from the field. I couldn't believe I would never see him again.

TRYING TO FORGET

Just to torture myself I would log onto the Hillside website to keep up-to-date with Jaffa and his friends. Amanda and I would text and email each other, comparing notes about Jaffa and Clown. I knew it would be better if I didn't visit the website, if I put my riding holiday behind me and tried to forget about Jaffa, but I couldn't. It was as if he was calling to me, reaching out to tell me something, something I couldn't understand.

THE WORST NEWS!

Then, one evening, when I thought my misery couldn't get worse, I read on the Hillside website that the centre was closing down. All the ponies were going to be sold – good homes were being sought for them all, including Jaffa. Of course, I burst into tears, and couldn't hide my misery from Mum and Dad, who demanded to know the reason for my unhappiness. When I told them, they exchanged looks, and I thought they were going to tell me to grow up, to pull myself together and forget a pony I had only known for a week last summer.

WERE WE TOO LATE?

But they didn't. Instead, they told me they had been thinking it was time I got my own pony, and did I want them to make enquiries about Jaffa?

Did I? My heart leapt – I couldn't believe my luck. But then it plummeted again, immediately. What if someone had already bought Jaffa? What if we were too late?

Mum rang Hillside there and then, and after a long discussion when I practically chewed off all my nails, she put the phone down and grinned at me.

"Jaffa's all yours," she said, "providing he passes the vetting!"

I burst into tears again, I was so happy.

A HAPPY ENDING

Jaffa's home now. He lives at a livery yard nearby and we have the best time. I've made friends with other girls, and Jaffa's made friends with their ponies, too. I can hardly believe how things have turned out. You just never know when you'll meet the pony of your dreams, do you?

Posed by models

Jaffa and I had the best time on my holiday

TAKE THE PONY ID CHALLENGE!

Okay, we're giving you the answers here – but you have to decide where they go! Are you up for the challenge?

Appaloosa

Bay roan

Piebald

Blue roan

Buckskin

Chestnut

Palomino

Dappled grey

Bay

Tri-coloured

APPALOOSA, BAY, BAY ROAN, BLUE ROAN, BUCKSKIN, CHESTNUT, DAPPLED GREY, PALOMINO, PIEBALD, TRI-COLOURED

Face-OFF

How many equine face markings do you know? Try these for size!

....Star and stripe...... .....Wide Blaze....

(answer key in circle:)
Wall eye
Mealy muzzle
Narrow blaze
Star and stripe
Stripe and snip
Extended star
Wide Blaze
Pink snip

......Pink snip...... ....Wall eye....

LEG IT!

See how many leg markings you can recognise!

White coronets, socks, ermine marks, stockings

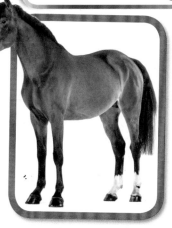

FRIENDS AND RELATIONS

Do you know your mules from your zebras? See if you can correctly identify these equine rels!

.....Donkey..... ....Zebra.....

Prezwalski's horse, zorse, donkey, mule, onager, zebra

.....Zorse.....

answers on page 98!

89

Duggie parle

DUGGIE AND THE COLONEL ARE BEING VERY ANNOYING BY TALKING IN FRENCH, WHICH SOLOMAN CAN'T UNDERSTAND. WILL HE GET HIS OWN BACK?

Ma Sœur a les cheveux bruns.

Really? I didn't know you had a sister. I mean, *pardon! Je ne savais pas que vous aviez une sœur!*

Ha, ha, ha...

Tee hee.

Buen día! Ole!

?

?

Still another language, though. One you *no* entiendes!

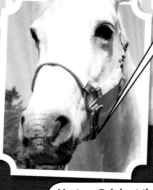

Aaaanyway, I'm fed up with this game.

Me too. Drink at the trough anyone?

Part 2
Français

DUGGIE

SOLOMAN

COLONEL

THE END

91

TROUBLE ON THE LAKE!

Charlie has an eventful boat ride...

HEY CHARLIE, AS IT'S SUCH A NICE DAY, SHALL WE GO FOR A WALK IN THE PARK?

I SUPPOSE WE COULD.

AWW LOOK AT ALL THE DUCKS WITH THEIR DUCKLINGS CHARLIE!

LET'S GO ROWING!

HI GUYS! LOOKING TO HIRE A BOAT TODAY?

YEAH!

HAS EITHER OF YOU ROWED BEFORE?

SURE! I KNOW WHAT I'M DOING!

HERE ARE YOUR LIFE JACKETS. I'LL JUST GET THE BOAT READY.

HA! CHARLENE YOU LOOK RIDICULOUS! I'M NOT WEARING MINE!

I WANT TO BE SAFE CHARLIE, WATER CAN BE DANGEROUS!

RIGHT YOU TWO, I'LL GIVE YOU A LITTLE PUSH AND THEN IT'S OVER TO YOU. HAVE FUN!

THIS IS LOVELY, WHAT A GREAT IDEA OF YOURS CHARLIE!

IT'S A BIT BORING REALLY...

UH-OH! IT LOOKS LIKE A STORM'S COMING, WE'D BETTER START ROWING BACK!

C'MON CHARLIE? GET ROWING!

JUST A SEC! YOU KNOW, I THINK I WILL PUT THAT LIFE JACKET ON!

OH CHARLIE! YOU KNOW I REALLY THINK ORANGE IS YOUR COLOUR!

92

15 things you hope no-one will ever say to you!

IS THAT ELLA'S OLD PONY? ONLY HE NEVER DID THAT WITH *HER*...

"When was the last time you didn't fall off on a lesson?"

OH IT ISN'T DIRT, THAT'S YOUR PONY'S ACTUAL COLOUR. WEIRD!

And you've had how many riding lessons?

CAN I BORROW YOUR PONY FOR PONY CLUB CAMP?

I had those jodhpurs when they were in fashion!

LET ME GIVE YOU MY INSTRUCTOR'S PHONE NUMBER – SHE'LL SORT YOU OUT IN NO TIME!

My pony did exactly the same thing until I learnt to ride properly.

Snowball never does that when I ride him...

I JUST LOVE COMING HOME FROM EVERY SHOW WITH ROSETTES. OH, YOU'VE NOT WON ONE BEFORE. SORRY!

WELL, YOU COULD DO IT LIKE THAT – BUT IT'S NOT THE WAY I'D DO IT...

AT LEAST YOU GOT OVER THE FIRST FENCE... SORT OF...

"I would lend you my jacket for the quadrille but you wouldn't get into it!

YOU CAME 4TH? I WON THAT CLASS ON THAT PONY LAST YEAR!

Stop! No... don't... Oh now look what you've done...

HOW WELL DO YOU KNOW YOUR FAVE PONY?

Take our fab quiz and find out how well you REALLY know your fave pony!

1. Do you know your fave pony's vital stats, like his show name, age, height, rug size etc?

🪶 Yes! I know it all and I have it all written down in my horsey diary!

🪬 **I know his name...**

🎩 I know most things about him I think, but not things like his rug size.

Is your pony a dressage diva...

...a show jumping enthusiast...

...or a XC nut?

2. How do you know which riding activity is your pony's fave?

🎩 He seems to like everything. He doesn't protest against anything.

🪬 Not sure – I just know he's cute!

🪶 He puts his ears forward and gets a bit stronger when we do things he likes, like hacking and jumping.

3. How much do you know about your fave pony's history?

🪶 I know where he was born and every yard he's ever lived at! I've got a copy of his family tree pinned on my wall.

🎩 I've met his previous owner and know he used to be a pretty good Pony Club pony, but that's about it.

🪬 I only know where he lives now, and that I met him. (Thank goodness!)

4. You always arrive at the yard armed with your fave pony's snack of choice, right?

🪬 All ponies love apples best, don't they?

🪶 Yep – he's partial to a particular brand of banana-flavour treats.

🎩 He never turns down anything minty!

5. You're asked to tack up your fave pony ready to be ridden. How does it go?

🪬 I remember he was wearing an orange numnah last time...

🪶 I know exactly what tack is his and I've memorised which buckle hole each strap goes on

🎩 I can tack him up, but I need help adjusting the straps to fit him.

6. You're out hacking on your fave pony when a tractor goes past in a nearby field. How will he react?

- I've not seen a tractor when riding before, but when I've seen other scary things he's fine if I stay calm and reassure him.
- I've never hacked him out before!
- He's never done anything scary before! He'll be fine.

Ponies find all different sorts of things scary!

7. It's 3pm. According to your fave pony's typical daily routine, what is he up to right now?

- Er, he might be eating something! He seems to like eating.
- Grazing. He's out in his field until 6pm. I know his routine inside out, and plan my day around it.
- I'm not sure. It depends on when he's ridden.

8. Do you know who your fave pony's best mates are?

- I know the names of all my fave pony's field mates and I try to hack out with them!
- He likes all ponies.
- He hangs out with a little brown-and-white pony a lot. Or is he black-and-white...?

A ride out with his mates = perfect!

"I even know what you're thinking..."

HOW DID YOU DO?

**Mostly ** Wow! You certainly know your fave pony inside out! You know all his likes, dislikes and habits, and you trust that you know what he'll do in a scary situation. Keep up the good work!

**Mostly ** You have a good bond with your fave pony, but there are still some things you don't know about him. Spend lots of time with him if you can, both riding and on the ground, and you'll soon become more familiar with every aspect of his personality.

**Mostly ** Uh-oh, do you even know this pony? You might think you know him, but is it just that you know general pony behaviour, and not behaviour specific to your fave pony? Keep spending time with him. Don't be afraid to ask the yard owner or his past owners lots of questions about him!

9. Could you take on the sole care of your fave pony with no help?

- I would like to try, but I might need some help to begin with until I settle into a routine.
- Definitely! I know every detail of my fave pony's routine and know exactly what care he needs.
- I know how to ride him and when he needs to be fed, but that's about it.

HORSES ON STAMPS!

People have been collecting stamps ever since the Penny Black was first issued in 1840!

Want to give it a go?

If you think collecting stamps is for you, you simply need a stamp album, a magnifying glass to see them properly and a pair of tweezers to handle them with to kick-start your hobby. Oh, and then you need some stamps!

A new hobby!

Stamp collecting is a hobby anyone can take up – and there are *Philatelists* (stamp collectors) all over the world! There are so many designs, it pays to limit a collection to something which really appeals to you – which would be horses, obviously!

French donkey: 2004

Racing in Romania: 1974

Indian Marwari horses: 2009

English Shire horse: 1978

Russia: 1968

Arab horses on Cuban stamp: 1995

USA, comemorating 100-year anniversary of the Pony Express: 1960

Royal Canadian Mounted Police: 1935

Dressage in Poland: 1967

Racing in Hungary: 1971

Zebras in Liberia: 1971

Show jumping in Russia: 1982

Grey Arab, Russia: 1988

Mongolian Wild Horse, Bulgaria: 1980

New Zealand: 1984

Icelandic horse: 1958

Swedish ponies: 1992

Tanzania: 1993

Benin: 1996

We've found images of horses on stamps from around the world to whet your appetite. Find stamps at stamp fairs, stamp markets and on the internet. Ebay often has horsey stamps on offer.

Old vs new

As well as old stamps, look out for first day covers. When a new set of stamps is issued, you can buy a commemorative set from the Post Office.

Artwork on stamps is representative of it's time – and each is a mini work of art in its own right!

Rwanda: 2013

Mustang horse

...ages: Rook 76, Neftall, Yangchao, Maxim Ibragimov, Andy Lidstone, Grisha Bruev, Solodov Alexey, Pete Spiro, Bons 15, Galyamin Sergej, Lefteris Papaulakis and Shutterstock.com

THE ANSWERS!

HOW DID YOU DO IN OUR QUIZZES? FIND OUT HERE!

Did you get all the points of the horse, saddle and bridle right? Check out your answers here.

POINTS OF A HORSE

1 Ear 2 Poll 3 Crest 4 Mane 5 Shoulder 6 Withers 7 Back 8 Loins 9 Croup 10 Dock 11 Point of Hip 12 Flank 13 Point of Buttocks 14 Tail 15 Thigh 16 Gaskin 17 Hock 18 Stifle 19 Elbow 20 Chestnut 21 Cannon Bone 22 Pastern 23 Heel 24 Wall of Hoof 25 Coronet 26 Fetlock 27 Knee 28 Forearm 29 Chest 30 Jaw 31 Cheek 32 Chin Groove 33 Mouth 34 Muzzle 35 Nostril 36 Eye 37 Forelock.

SADDLE PARTS

38 Cantle 39 Panel 40 Seat 41 Flap 42 Waist 43 Knee Roll 44 Skirt 45 Pommel

INDENTI-BRIDLE

46 Noseband 47 Flash Noseband 48 Loose-ring Snaffle 49 Reins 50 Throatlash 51 Cheekpiece 52 Browband 53 Headpiece.

Yard hazards test. How many did you spot?

HAZARD TEST

1. Dangling headcollar
2. Hoof pick left on the ground
3. Mounting block left out
4. Haynet on the ground
5. Swinging stable door
6. Rug with straps left dangling
7. Poo picker fallen over and not picked up
8. Hose unravelled
9. Open feed bag left out
10. Baler twine left on the ground
11. Brush left in the yard

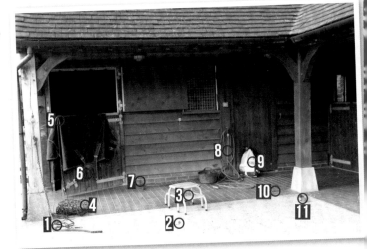

Our Famous Rider Gridword was tricky. How did you do?
1. Charlotte *Dujardin*. 2. Jessica *Mendoza*. 3. John *Whitaker*. 4. Piggy *French*. 5. Oliver *Townend*. 6. Pippa *Funnell*. 7. Natasha *Baker*. 8. Ben *Maher*. 9. Lucinda *Fredericks*. 10. Harry *Meade*. 11. Mary *King*. 12. Carl *Hester*. 13. Laura *Collett*. 14. Scott *Brash*. 15. Tim *Stockdale*.

BREED QUIZ

Did you work out all the breeds? Here are the answers.
1. Exmoor. 2. Highland. 3. Friesian. 4. Missouri Fox-Trotter. 5. Quarter Horse. 6. Fell. 7. New Forest. 8. Suffolk Punch. 9. Hackney. 10. Trakehner.

SPOT THE DIFFERENCE

Here are the solutions!

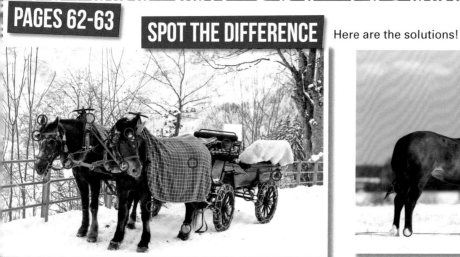

How did you do in our Pony ID Challenge? Time to find out!

Appaloosa

Bay Roan

Blue Roan

Buckskin

Palomino

Dappled Grey

Tri-coloured

Bay

Chestnut

Piebald

LEG IT!

Ermine Marks   White Coronets   Stockings   Socks

FRIENDS AND RELATIONS

Donkey   Prezwalski's Horse   Zebra

Onager   Zorse   Mule

FACE-OFF

Extended Star   Star and Stripe   Mealy muzzle   Wide Blaze

Narrow Blaze   Pink snip   Stripe and Snip   Wall Eye

THE END-OF-THE-ANNUAL QUIZ!

IT'S NOT OVER YET! CHECK YOU'VE BEEN PAYING ATTENTION WITH OUR END-OF-THE-ANNUAL QUIZ. THE ANSWERS CAN ONLY BE FOUND IN THE ANNUAL ITSELF — WE'RE NOT GIVING THEM TO YOU HERE, THAT WOULD BE TOO EASY! GOOD LUCK!

1 Why should you bank the sides of a pony's bed in the stable?

....

2 What should you do with your pony's bridle after every ride, even if you don't have time to clean his tack?

....

3 Name three rules of the school.

....
....
....

4 How do show cobs wear their manes?

....

5 What is a traditional cob?

....

6 When riding as a pair, what part of their bodies should the riders try to get in line?

....

7 Can you describe the design of Charlie's onesie?

....
....

8 How often do ponies think about eating?

....

9 Do ponies sleep overnight as we do, or do they take naps throughout the day and night?

....

10 Can ponies breathe through their mouths?

....

11 How should a rider use their legs? Inwards, or backwards?

INWARDS ☐

BACKWARDS ☐

12 What is the name for the back of the saddle?

....
....